SIX TO BREAK EVEN

by

MARY
SCOTT
ADAMS

RAND McNALLY & COMPANY
New York · CHICAGO · San Francisco

While most of the episodes in this story are auto-
biographical the characters are a composite of many
different people whose paths we crossed during our
years of farming. No character in this book represents
or is intended to represent any actual person, living
or dead.

INTRODUCTION

Toward the end of the 1930's we were licking what we hoped would be the last wounds inflicted by the Depression, wondering if the ebullient gaiety of the twenties was gone forever. With fringe leaping and feet snapping we had Charlestoned away our teens, unaware of the piper around the corner waiting to demand payment for our noteworthy irresponsibility.

Gone were the speakeasies and bathtub gin, those bottles of alcohol smelling like porch varnish that we carried home from a variety of sources and flavored with juniper, orgeat syrup, or bourbaline. There was no more sneaking a drink in broom closets at dances, in the back seat of automobiles under an outstretched overcoat; no more toting flasks to nightclubs to get high on drinks originating under the table. The restaurants serving martinis in after-dinner coffee cups during Prohibition now had respectable, rather dull bars.

In the thirties drinking, like living, wasn't much fun.

Lamb chops were six cents apiece; you could buy a new car under five hundred dollars, a winter coat for seventeen, a summer suit for eight, and department store bargain sales offered real bargains. The dollar was mighty, but scarce.

Like us, everybody we knew was busted. Many of our friends had disappeared to unannounced addresses; some were sharing crowded quarters with intolerant in-laws. All of us lived with a perpetual cloud of financial worry over our heads.

We were just barely making our way on Charles' drawing account at the brokerage firm of Thurston, Dalton and Company. The months he didn't make his drawing account we shuddered and thought of the apple sellers on street corners.

Charles and I, our twelve-year-old daughter, Maria, and nine-year-old Jan were living in Winnetka, in the house Charles had borrowed the money to build; he claimed it would be cheaper than paying rent, and eventually we would have an equity in real property.

The house, designed by a college friend of my husband's who had managed to get an architectural degree at night school, was his first. He did it for nothing. It was as slender and racy-looking as an oceangoing yacht, and quite a bit longer. The furnace at the kitchen end was incapable of blowing sufficient heat past the front hall, so the temperature in the living room and the music room beyond rarely got above 55 degrees from November to April. The architect insisted on the music room although none of us played anything. He also insisted that the plans include round, aquarium-like windows, flamboyant turrets, and such "interesting" breaks in the linear structure as a jutting glass orangery, a mud room, and a sulking corner which was contained within a huge banjo bay. Instead of a pantry off the kitchen, he designed a combination sewing and hair-drying room for me.

Unfortunately this agreeable and nutty young man died in an automobile accident before the roof got on the house. The contractor with the granite countenance of Sitting Bull, having an abhorrence for what he called doodads, cut from the plans all the "interesting" innovations of the design. He simply built a two-story brick and clapboard rectangle about five times as long as it was wide. He called it a typical Illinois farmhouse which wasn't at all what any of us had in mind in the beginning.

The basement leaked, the sump pump stuck, the windows refused to open, and the tiles to the septic tank were pitched *toward* the house. At our housewarming the downstairs toilet overflowed into a lava-like encroachment of sewage which slowly covered the beveled oak floors in the front hall and mingled with the mud brought in on the feet of a hundred guests dressed for the occasion in cutaways and long velvet cocktail dresses.

My thirtieth birthday, like a mirrored grimace in the fun house, was staring me in the face. Thirty! That was the age, everyone always said, when a woman was at her best. I heard it when I was a pimply fourteen, when I was a confused seventeen, wearing false bangs and a pearl-studded Spanish comb for confidence, and during my twenties when I was in and out of hospitals having babies and miscarriages.

"Just wait," I was told by encouraging tongues, "until you are thirty! It is the age when a woman is mature, but still beautiful; experienced, yet not tarnished by living; sexually desirable, with an attraction no young girl can hope to have." (The Lolitas had not yet reared their horrid little heads.) I believed them, fancying myself a seductive thirty, flung across a pink satin Récamier, scantily clad in chiffon pantaloons, and heavily bejeweled like Theda Bara and the sirens on the candy box lids of my childhood.

What I'd been told proved chimerical. How could I be seductive when my life combined the action of the sturdy, white-bonneted figure, stick in hand, chasing dirt on cans of Old Dutch Cleanser, and a driver for Wells Fargo whipping the horses in our old, exhausted Ford? How could I possibly be desirable tearing between commuter platforms, the public library, schools, doctors' and dentists' offices, and Brownie outings in the forest preserve, with in-between stops at the A&P and Pop Gruder's vegetable stand?

I would simply have to put it off for the time being, I told myself, not foreseeing the ax which fell one chilly April evening when I met Charles at the station. It lopped off all hope of ever wearing rings on my toes.

CHAPTER
1

The instant Charles swung off the 5:35 I knew it had been no ordinary day downtown. He always looked as if he was climbing out of a leaky sleeping bag when he got off that train, but that night his eyes were looped with circles as black as a raccoon's, and his lips, usually parted in a cheerful, weary grin, appeared to be stitched together in a fine hard line.

Back at the house he threw his *Wall Street Journal* and *Daily News* on Aunt Millicent's rosewood settee in the hall, dumped his overcoat on the papers, and crowned the heap with his hat as he always does, but his embrace was tepid. He ignored Jan, who held out to him a skirtful of her new baby hamsters, and he barely nodded at Maria inside the bulk of her new football uniform she'd ordered from the Sears, Roebuck catalog. Without a word, without taking off his stiff collar, he vanished into his study and stirred up a pitcher of martinis.

"He won't be any fun tonight," Maria remarked to her younger sister. "Either the dumb stock market has gone down again, or he's been dieting. Let's go up and listen to Jack Armstrong."

When we sat down with our drinks Charles replied to the unasked question burning my tongue. "It's Uncle Henry's farm," he said, slowly patting the top of his head as he does when preoccupied.

"What about Uncle Henry's farm?"

"He's left it to me. The will was read this morning."

"Oh, no!" I was stupefied. "You always acted too damned interested in that ghastly farm!" I regretted my words immediately as Charles' weary face winced from the final lash of the beating he'd been taking all day.

"I was interested in it. I still am," he declared, summoning a note of determination to his tired voice. "Agriculture is the world's oldest profession, with the possible exception of Mrs. Warren's, and I've always wanted to try my hand at it. But when I consider the money Uncle Henry spent on his farm without ever showing a profit I get financial chills."

"He didn't leave you any money?"

Charles shook his head.

"He might at least have left enough to keep the place going. Like an endowment for a museum."

"That would have been nice." Charles refilled his glass.

"Maybe you can sell it?"

"I wish to God I could, but it's not that easy. People are being pretty careful what they buy. I've spent most of the day talking to fellows in the real estate business. They're very pessimistic."

"Suppose you forget all about it and just let it sit there; maybe the land will appreciate in value some day."

"I've thought of that too, but if I do that all the money Uncle Henry poured into it will be wasted. The fertilizer will leach away, the buildings will go to pieces, and so will the machinery and the new fences. If the farm isn't worked it will go to pot."

"Good."

"It isn't good at all. We're going to have to carry on where Uncle Henry left off."

"You don't mean we're going to have to live on that pile of filthy sand?"

"Weekends, vacations, bank holidays—whenever I can get away from my office."

10

In the kitchen I lifted the lid of the Dutch oven and peered through the steam at the pot roast. When it was put on it looked big enough to stretch to two, maybe even three meals, but it had shrunk to a small brown fist. Was it an omen? A manifestation of what was going to happen to our meager budget carefully measured each month into payments on the house, insurance, dancing lessons for the girls, orthodontists, a bottle of whiskey, and two nights at the movies? How could we possibly take on the additional expense of farming two thousand acres of land that wouldn't grow dandelions?

Peeling the vegetables I tried not to think harshly of Uncle Henry. Any man who had worked so hard and had been so successful in business was entitled to one white elephant, but the trouble with white elephants was that they didn't always die with you. They were apt to survive to trample someone else's life.

Knowing what a liability his farm would impose on Charles, why did Uncle Henry leave it to him? Why hadn't he left it to his sons or his daughter who as his beneficiaries were well-heeled? Perhaps at the end of his life he didn't care; he didn't care about a lot of things. Yet, he was devoted to Charles, the only child of his younger sister whom he had raised as his own son after Charles' mother and father were lost on the *Titanic* in 1912.

Charles, a boy of eight, went to live with Uncle Henry and Aunt Charlotte in their gray stone mansion in Kenwood on Chicago's South Side, growing up in a world of starched efficiency provided by a succession of Irish nannies.

Aunt Charlotte's health did not permit her to do more than make an occasional inquiry into the welfare of her children in the nursery. Sometimes she read to them a few verses of Eugene Field, and she heard their prayers at bedtime. Once in a great while she took the older ones for a drive through Washington Park in her Milburn Light Electric, fragrant with violets in the crystal vase hung in the pearl gray interior, but by the standards of her time Aunt Charlotte was considered an invalid. None of the doctors Uncle Henry called in seemed to know what was the matter with her. Unable to diagnose a specific illness, they agreed she was very frail and suffered from chronic exhaustion, but from what Charles and his cousins said, it wasn't difficult to believe that life with Uncle Henry was too much for her. His overwhelming presence wore her out as, to a lesser degree, it did the other members of his household.

When Uncle Henry opened his eyes in the morning it was as if a switch were thrown sending a current crackling throughout the entire house. His first act was to fling open his bedroom door and shout for his male children, who tumbled half asleep down the stairs from their quarters on the third floor. Lining them up in front of the opened window at the foot of the brass bed where Aunt Charlotte lay grasping a bottle of smelling salts, he handed around the Indian clubs he kept under the bed. With his nightshirt flapping against his powerful legs he swung the clubs in furious circles, demanding the same physical aptitude from the boys. At the end of ten minutes he panted, "Bully exercise!" dropped the clubs, and dove into the old-fashioned marble bathroom to ready himself for the day.

At breakfast, under the Tiffany glass shade suspended from the paneled ceiling in the dining room, he gave a booming account of the problems waiting for him at his office downtown and at the plant in Pullman. He described the care he must take figuring bids on contracts, or else "those fellers" would steal his eyeballs. He spoke of "the ginks" at his plant who didn't know an angle iron from a channel beam unless he was there to tell them. Each new day was his private battlefield swarming with a variety of enemies who must be subdued if he were to survive.

12

His New England ancestors had given him the rugged constitution he stoked every morning with generous portions of oatmeal, codfish cakes, and creamed chipped beef which the second maid circulated around the table at a dogtrot. Chewing and talking at the same time he left the table to stride into the hall where he exchanged the napkin tucked in his waistcoat for his greatcoat and astrakhan hat. Shoving a roll of blueprints under his arm, he went out the front door like a gust of north wind, calling over his shoulder enough orders to insure that his family and staff would be as occupied throughout the day as he was going to be. The moment the door closed behind him the children let out an involuntary sigh and dropped their shoulders, and Aunt Charlotte got undressed and went back to bed.

Precisely at seven o'clock the old warrior's key opened the front door. Divesting himself of his outer armor, he washed his hands in the lavatory under the golden oak staircase before charging into the dining room. His family was assembled at the table, awaiting his arrival before removing their napkins from the silver rings. Like a pin to a magnet Uncle Henry went to the sideboard, filled a shot glass with bourbon whiskey from the decanter, threw it down in a single gulp, and saying "aaah," seated himself at the head of the table. He inquired immediately what everyone had accomplished that day beginning with Aunt Charlotte, who of course hadn't done anything, and going clockwise around the table to Robert, Henry, Jr., his only daughter, Millicent and, finally, Charles, seated at Aunt Charlotte's right. After suggesting certain improvements they might make in the future, he resumed the recitation of his own problems begun at breakfast, explaining exactly how he had dealt with every circumstance.

After dinner he took his violin from its black leather case flakey with age and while Aunt Charlotte played timidly on the piano *The Album of Old Favourites,* he sawed lustily on the strings, tapping his foot on the Oriental rug in time to the music. In a rusty bass he joined the medley of his children's voices ranging from a choir soprano to the rasping uncertainty of adolescence.

Two nights a week he played auction bridge with his cronies in the neighborhood. He would return at midnight and climb into bed, embracing Aunt Charlotte until she woke up and had to listen to the remarkable distribution of cards in a particular hand and how he had coped with it. Uncle Henry's compulsion to share with others whatever he was doing or thinking was absolute.

By the time I started going out with Charles, Uncle Henry was an old man, disillusioned by what he called a lack of red blood in his sons and nephew who had refused the silver platter opportunity of carrying on his construction business, preferring less robust careers in law offices and investment banking houses. It was the fault of the colleges these days, he grunted, teaching a lot of newfangled hoopla that turned boys into sissies instead of men.

He was infuriated by the rise in taxes, and the way the government was robbing the rich to give to the poor who, he declared, had probably never done an honest day's work in their lives.

He was as restless as a hungry lion after he sold the business none of the boys wanted. He was as lonely as a hermit without Aunt Charlotte who had been gathered up by the angels some years before when her Light Electric jumped the curb in front of the German Building and turned over on its square glass side.

Perhaps if he had bought the farm sooner he would have been happier, for during the four years he lived to enjoy it he became his old self again, vigorously attacking the assignment of farming land that refused to support crops.

He poured fertilizer into the substandard soil, planted

14

locust trees to hold the ever-shifting sand, and set out acres of apple orchards and raspberries he called Cuthberts. He acquired a dairy herd headed by a Holstein bull named Oliver whose eyes were as red as carnations and whose satanic disposition was a threat to anyone who came near him. When Uncle Henry thought the creamery in the town of Zulu wasn't paying him enough for his produce, he bought that, too. He obtained by persuasive methods contracts from restaurants in Chicago to buy his butter, but after several deliveries it was returned to him with the complaint that it was full of splinters. He had scraped the vats too thin.

He planned to "camp out" with his chauffeur over weekends in the house he built for himself on the farm, but after a couple of times the chauffeur declined to return, declaring that sleeping with a bunch of bawling cows wasn't his idea of the way to spend Saturday night. After that Uncle Henry drove his limousine to the farm himself. I went with him a few times to keep him company on the journey, most of which was made in second gear. He was so absorbed in his plans for improving his farm he would forget to shift into high.

It was inconceivable to me that a man of his age with a lifetime of business experience behind him could exhibit such enthusiasm for a spread of sandy land dotted with rotting buildings. How could he hope to make it produce anything? It was as dismal, as undernourished in appearance as my imagined picture of a county poor farm. Yet there was not a doubt he had a very real affection for it.

Oddly enough the small frame house he'd built burned to the ground the night after Uncle Henry died. The only things that were saved were the stuffed tarpon he'd caught one winter in Boca Grande that had hung over the fireplace, and the running-board trunk off his 1929 Pierce Arrow that he had used as a file cabinet.

At the time of his death Uncle Henry was in Paris on one

of his infrequent visits to his cousin, Will Webb, whom he despised as a loafer. Cousin Will, a bachelor, inherited from the New England family estate an income permitting him to live in Sicily in the winter and to maintain a Paris apartment in the summer. Cousin Will enjoyed the mild climate of Syracuse which he pronounced "Syracoosa," infuriating Uncle Henry, and he interested himself in paintings, music, and reading French history when in Paris.

Cousin Will had taken Uncle Henry and Henry, Jr., who accompanied him, on a sightseeing tour of the city in an attempt to amuse his hardheaded Yankee cousin. The three men, according to Henry, Jr., were standing on *le pont du Trocadero* gazing at the Eiffel Tower when Uncle Henry spoke his last words: "If I didn't know I was in Paris, I'd think I was in Texas. That thing looks like an oversized oil derrick."

Cousin Will considered the remark for a moment. When he turned to reply, Uncle Henry was not at his side. He was a heap of crumpled gray overcoat on the pavement. "It was," Henry, Jr., reported, "as if the Texans had risen up in anger and retaliated with a single stroke."

I was eighteen when Charles and I became engaged. I was looking forward to some kind of father-daughter relationship with Uncle Henry and to having a normal family life with Charles' cousins. Our father, who sired my sister Connie the first year of his marriage to Mamma, and me six years later, died when I was a few months old. His disappointment in not producing the son he wanted so badly might have had something to do with his death. Maybe when he looked at another fat baby girl with smeary black hair he lost interest in living. Anyway, I had always wanted a father to see what it would be like to have a male parent as well as Mamma who was twenty-five years younger than the faded sepia photograph I learned to call "Daddy" as soon as I could talk.

Widowed at thirty-five, Mamma had no further reason to remain in Chicago, so she devoted her life to travel, taking with her Connie and me and Aunt, her older sister. During her peregrinations she had many opportunities to remarry, for she was the kind of woman who attracted men without bothering to try. With her green eyes, her auburn hair, pearl-button teeth, throaty laugh, and exquisite figure she was courted from Maine to California.

Connie and I hoped she would marry Mr. de Liese who was Swiss and lived in Newport in the summer and New York in the winter. He had a mane of white hair, a pistachio-colored moustache, and he used a monocle. In addition to these appealing qualities he was very rich, which would have helped a lot because we were having to cut down more and more all the time. Daddy's investments weren't the kind that stood up very long and those that did were forever passing their dividends. Connie maintained that the reason Mamma never remarried was because Aunt, a confirmed spinster, talked her out of it.

Aunt, with her prominent jaw and her wispy hair pulled up on top of her head into a flat pancake, never had any use for men. Perhaps it was because she lacked Mamma's beauty and her talent to attract them, but she had other capabilities. She could cook, after a fashion, iron ribbons, and imitate birdcalls. Pursing her colorless lips beneath her Woodrow Wilson pince-nez she would emit ear-piercing interpretations of the mockingbird, the robin, canaries, and the bobwhite quail. When she did the cardinal everyone in the room broke out in gooseflesh. Also, Aunt composed a piano concerto she called "Inskyoff's Parade," which she performed fortissimo whenever we lived in a place that had a piano.

At the time of our engagement the two families observed the tribal custom of dining at one another's homes — ours was a furnished apartment on the Near North Side of Chicago at the time — making inane conversation all the while sizing up the opposition. When it was our turn Mamma bought a bottle of bootleg champagne she could ill afford. She served it with one of Aunt's half-ton sponge cakes, but Uncle Henry announced that champagne gave him heartburn, and he toasted the happy couple with his water glass. However, he was obviously attracted to Mamma, and when we were at his house he gave her as a token of his esteem twelve yellow tomatoes he picked from his garden.

Mamma, not one to be taken in, remarked when we got home, "The boy is rather sweet, Mary, but that old man is a curmudgeon. I hear he's fearfully rich, but tight as the bark on a tree. Don't expect to get any money from him, especially since you are marrying his nephew and not one of his sons."

I didn't care about money then. I was in love with Charles, and I wanted to mean something to Uncle Henry even though his gruffness terrified me. When he wasn't being gruff he would stare hard at me finally terminating his staring with a loud grunt.

When I carried the fist-sized pot roast to the table Charles and the girls were talking about the farm. Jan was begging for a pony now there was a place to keep one, and Maria was asking if there were any kids in Zulu, Indiana, for her to jelly around with.

"We'll see," Charles replied. "Tomorrow is Saturday, and we'll drive down and look things over."

"I can't go tomorrow," Maria said through and around a mouthful of food.

"Why not?"

"The sixth grade boys are playing the seventh grade boys and I'm pitching."

"In a boy's game?"

"Sure. I've got a neater knuckleball than any of those

guys." With her greasy fingers she pushed back the leather football helmet that had settled over her eyes.

"Does she always have to eat dinner in a football uniform?" Charles looked at me appealingly.

"Why not ask her?"

"Do you?" He regarded Maria with discouragement. "In the first place you're a girl and it doesn't become you. In the second place the football season was over in December. This is April."

"I'm breaking it in for fall," Maria replied. "It's stiff."

"It's all right to be a tomboy, I suppose," Charles continued, "if you don't carry it too far. I once knew a girl who worked on motors and machinery parts all day. She was a wizard at it, but she looked like a grease monkey. None of the boys would dance with her at parties."

"Duuah," Maria drawled insultingly. "Who wants to dance with boys?"

"What happened to the girl, Daddy?" Jan's sense of the dramatic demanded a suitable ending to every story. "Didn't she get married or anything?"

"Yes, she married. She married the son of Uncle Henry's chauffeur. She wore a white wedding gown over her coveralls with a monkey wrench stuck in her back pocket."

"How did you *know* there was a monkey wrench in her coveralls?"

"Because I was at the wedding. When she and her bridegroom knelt down in front of the minister, the wrench dropped out on the stone floor of the church."

"How revolting!" Jan exclaimed. "You'd better be careful, Maria. You're almost as disgusting right now."

"Shut up or I'll kill you," Maria replied laconically.

"That's enough," Charles admonished. "We'll leave at noon tomorrow. After the game."

"Maria has a two o'clock ballet lesson," I reminded him.

19

"Ballet? Maria?" Charles looked incredulous.

"Ballet stinks," Maria declared. "All you do is walk around on tiptoes holding a balloon over your head to make you graceful. Personally I think it's a waste of time."

"Well," said her father in the spirit of stern Agrippa, "I'm leaving for the farm at noon, and anyone who wants to come along had better be ready."

CHAPTER
2

The land from which the highway town of Zulu, Indiana, sprang was a lake before someone got the idea of draining the lake into the Kankakee River and making tillable soil of its questionable bottom. The result was Muskrat County, a slough of marshy lumps, nodding cattails, and saw grass obviously unpalatable to the undernourished livestock wandering listlessly behind strands of barbed wire in search of a mouthful of decent grazing. Punctuating the marshes were long stretches of sand beach more adaptable to bathing suits than the miserable crops trying to get a root system established before the wind shifted the sand and uncovered them altogether.

Four miles south of Zulu a gravel county road met the highway. It was the turnoff to Uncle Henry's farm. As the car bumped over the duck nests, a powdery white dust seeped up through the floor of the car and in through the windows even though they were rolled up tight. By the time we reached the entrance to the farm, we looked as if we'd been put in a sack of flour and shaken vigorously.

The entrance to the farm was marked by a large dead tree whose naked branches rattled like a bouquet of long black bones against the sky. Under the tree there was a big yellow rock, said to be a fallen meteor. The Cant-Sag gate, belying its name, had come loose from its moorings to a listing railroad tie and slumped to the ground.

"I can't imagine why Uncle Henry didn't fix this up a

bit," Charles remarked, turning into the cinder lane where the farm buildings were visible in the distance. "If we take out that old tree, put up a new gate and plant some bushes, lilacs, maybe, or rose bushes, it would look a lot better."

"How are you going to carry water to the rose bushes way out here?" Maria inquired. (She received 25 cents a week for watering the garden in Winnetka.)

Charles did not reply. He drove past the slatted corn-cribs, two weather-beaten sheds holding one another up like a pair of congenial drunks, a gas pump, and an apron of broken concrete which was the remains of a hog-feeding compound long abandoned. He finally came to a stop in the barnlot carpeted with wall-to-wall sand. The black dust swirling up from the cinders in the lane, on top of the white powder from the road, gave the impression we were uniformly dressed in salt and pepper tweeds as we got out of the car.

"It's so dirty here, Daddy," Jan exclaimed, cuffing at the dust on her Best and Company navy reefer.

"Never mind. You'll get used to it."

"Gee," Maria said, sucking in her breath as she ran her clear brown eyes over the old red barn crowned with turquoise ball-lightning rods, "that's neat!" She turned her head to stare at the twin silos casting serpentine shadows across the wavy sand. "What are those things for?"

"Silage."

"What's silage?"

"I'll explain it to you later. Not now," her father replied.

"It must have something to do with sex," Jan commented.

Charles didn't hear her. He stood in a trance shielding his eyes from the sun and gazing beyond the barnlot at the several dunes on which sheds, small barns, and houses perched like dusty ornaments on bakery window cakes. "It's

22

great, isn't it?" he muttered. His feet sunk deep in the sand were invisible so that it seemed as if he had taken root and was growing. "That's where the farmer, Art Schlager, lives." He nodded at the dune, overlooking the barnlot that supported the original farm dwelling, a large white-shingled house. Many shingles had been ripped off by wind and weather, so that the sides of the house looked like a piano keyboard with a lot of the white keys missing. On top of the roof a windowed cupola was enclosed by a square of iron railing on the verge of collapse.

"I'm going up to see Art. Why don't you girls walk up to the little house on that hill? That's where we'll live when we're down here. You might want to make some curtains or something to brighten it up."

"Well, duuah," Maria said. "Who wants to make curtains?"

While Charles snowplowed up the big dune the girls and I dragged our feet up a smaller hill through the sand sprouting a meager cover of weeds. The house was a cube-shaped bungalow which, in its paintless condition, was the color of driftwood. We sat down on the back steps to empty our shoes; there was a screech of nails pulling out of rotten lumber. A second later the steps fell off the house, pitching us to the ground.

"Ouch!" Jan cried, scrambling to her feet. "This is positively dangerous! This house must be haunted. Do you think anybody has ever *lived* here, Mummy?"

"Of course they have! Uncle Henry's chicken specialist lived here the summer he decided to raise Rhode Island Reds."

"What happened to him?"

"The chickens got something called Newcastle disease and died. Uncle Henry was so mad he fired the man."

"Let's go inside." Maria scaled up the clapboard siding

and grabbed the back door knob. At her touch the door came off and crashed to the ground, sending up a spray of glass splinters from the panel in the top. "Duuah," she drawled, unperturbed, and climbed through the doorframe into the house pulling us up after her with her strong right arm.

"What's that thing?" She nodded at a pump fastened to the stained kitchen sink.

"A water pump, I suppose." I took hold of the handle and worked it up and down. Not a drop of water came out of the rusty spout.

"This is goofy!" She called from the next room. "Here is a perfectly good bathroom with a tub and everything. If there's a bathroom, why hasn't the kitchen got running water?"

Jan and I peered into the bathroom while Maria worked the faucets on the washbasin. Nothing happened.

"It's like the rural parts of Mexico," she declared. "The people have bathrooms but hardly any water. We've been reading about it in social studies. They just enjoy looking at their tiled bathrooms even though they don't work."

As she spoke a loud gasp came from a pipe under the house. The washstand shuddered on its spindled legs, the faucets coughed, and into the bowl dribbled a trickle of nut-brown water.

"Let it run," I suggested. "Maybe it will clear up."

We moved into the next room.

"Is this a bed?" Jan demanded, putting her hand on a brass bedstead held together here and there with tarnished knobs.

"Of course it's a bed. It's exactly like the one Uncle Henry and Aunt Charlotte slept in."

"No wonder they're both dead," Maria observed, stooping to pick up the knobs that had fallen off and rolled across the bare floor.

Jan stood in front of a dirty window and scooped

24

handfuls of sand from the sill. "Look at this! How did the sand get inside when the window was closed?"

"It seeps," Maria explained. "Like the dust did through the windows of the car."

In the living room a faded blue velour sofa and matching chair stared dispassionately at one another, shedding their kapok stuffing on the linoleum rug. On one wall of the small square room a coal stove stood on an asbestos mat. On the opposite wall a massive wardrobe rose to the smoke-darkened ceiling, its yawning doors revealing an old pair of work shoes lying toe to toe on one of the shelves.

"Look on the floor in the corner!" Jan exclaimed. "There's enough sand to fill a sandbox. Jeepers."

"This must be the dining room," Maria called from the next room. "There's a table and chair and a funny-looking cupboard with busted cups and saucers."

"A dining room we don't need," I told her. "That can be your room, yours and Jan's. We'll get a double-decker for it."

"Dibs on the upper," Maria responded.

The tour completed, we went out the front door and sat down warily on the front steps.

"What are you going to do, Mummy?" Jan asked.

"Think."

"What are you going to think about?"

"I'm going to think how in hell I can make this goddamned place livable."

"*Mummy!*" Jan giggled.

"You two go and explore. I'll wait here for your father."

The girls ran with difficulty through the deep sand, tripping over bull nettles, falling down, and picking themselves up. Their clothes were already so dirty they would probably have to be burned, I reflected as my eyes wandered over the distant fields where whirlwinds of sand were rising in miniature tornado funnels.

The buildings in the foreground sagged forlornly on

their weathered foundations as if they had long ago given up feeling useful, and were now waiting for a wind strong enough to topple them over so they could rest in peace. The place looked even more run down and dejected than I remembered when I drove down with Uncle Henry. The twin concrete silos near the barnlot were the only solid, worthwhile buildings on the farm, and they were empty.

Well, there was nothing I could do about the farm, I told myself. My province was the house. I began a list of things we would need for it. While I was writing, Charles returned and sat down beside me on the steps. His face was blackened by muck dirt, his trousers were caked with mud up to the knees, and a pocket was torn halfway off his Christmas jacket from Abercrombie's I had saved four months to buy. He'd been out in the fields with Art, he explained, and had slipped off the ditch bank into the muddy creek.

"There's a lot more muck land than I thought," he declared. "The land that isn't muck is black sand. That's what blows so badly, but Art says when the crops are up it doesn't blow so much."

"What crops?"

"Corn. Art says we ought to plant most of the fields in corn with a few acres of oats."

"The fields haven't been plowed, have they?"

Charles shook his dirty head. "No, and they should have been by now. It seems that Art doesn't make a move until he's told to. He also said the dairy herd was infected, and the examiners won't let us sell any more milk. He says we'll have to get rid of the cows and Oliver, the bull. Art claims we should have a beef herd anyway, to utilize the roughage which dairy cows can't do. Also some steers in the feedlot. Then we can run hogs after them."

"What do you mean, run hogs after them?"

"The hogs eat the undigested corn in the steer droppings. It saves a lot of feed."

"That's the most disgusting thing I've ever heard. I'll never eat another pork chop."

"You're being neurotic, Mary."

"Not any more neurotic than you planning to run hogs you haven't got after steers you haven't bought so they can eat undigested corn which isn't even planted."

"It'll take time, but we'll manage." He peered over my shoulder. "What are you writing?" He read my list aloud: "Paint house; get new sink; new icebox; new stove, heating plant; new back door; bathroom cabinet; double-decker bed; desk for Charles; wrought iron plant stand; new rugs throughout. Mary, have you gone out of your mind?"

"Have you examined the interior of our new country house? Try and make it habitable on less."

"We can't possibly afford all those things."

"I know it," I replied. "I was just amusing myself."

"We have to put what money we have in seed corn, building repairs, Art's wages, and a pump for the well house. The old one gave out. You'll just have to use whatever is inside the cottage, except the double-decker. That's for the girls isn't it?"

I nodded. "Unless you think I should get two. Have you seen the mattress on the bed in our room? It's not as thick as the blotter on your desk."

"I wouldn't like to sleep in a double-decker," Charles remarked sadly. "Can't you get a secondhand mattress somewhere?"

"I think I'll drive out to Woodstock tomorrow and look for some bargains at Mrs. Snookey's."

"You haven't forgotten the dinner party?"

"What dinner party?"

"I told you last week the Kunkels were coming in from New York. O. G. is going to conduct the sales meeting Monday morning, and I invited him and his wife and Gil and Bob from the office with their wives for dinner Sunday night."

"You never told *me*."

"Of course I did!"

"Well, I don't remember. Anyway we can't have them. There's nothing in the house, and by the time we get back to Winnetka all the stores will be closed."

"We'll stop at that chicken farm on Route 30 on the way home and buy some fryers. We have canned vegetables in the house, and I can get some ice cream at the drugstore when I take the kids to Sunday school in the morning."

"What about the booze? The last time O. G. came to the house he knocked off a fifth of Scotch all by himself. That was the night he was going to make you a partner, remember?"

"Listen, Mary, I know what a bore O. G. is, but he's the managing partner. He didn't make me a partner, it's true, but I think he likes me, and he could put in a good word for me at the Chicago office that might mean a raise, or at least a bonus at Christmas. We can't afford not to entertain him when he's out here even though I realize it will shoot the budget for a month."

"Does O. G. know you are about to become an agricultural specialist in addition to being a stock and bond salesman?"

"No, and for God's sake, don't mention the farm. O. G. might think of it as a divided interest. He likes his men to hit the ball exclusively for Thurston, Dalton and Company. He likes them to work for the firm all day and dream about it all night."

"Look what's coming." I nudged Charles and pointed to our children slowly making their way toward us from the hen house in back of the Schlagers. They looked as if they had been tarred and feathered. Their clothes were in shreds. Jan's long blond hair was plastered across her sticky cheeks, and Maria was holding a bloody right arm with a bloody left hand.

"What in heaven's name have you been doing?" Charles turned his blackened face toward his daughters.

"Making egg pies in the sand," Maria replied. "It was Jan's idea."

"We found a kind of house with little boxes full of eggs that were just left there. We broke the eggs in the sand and made custard pies," Jan related.

"You took the eggs from the nests?" Charles was horrified by their wantonness.

"Nobody seemed to want them. Nobody that is, except one mean old chicken. When Maria put her hand under it to pick up the eggs it flew up in our faces and scratched Maria something awful. She's probably got Newcastle disease right now. Maybe she'll have to have her arm amputated."

While Charles lectured the children I took a final look inside the dismal house. The county poorhouse couldn't have depressed me more. Turning off the brown dribble in the bathroom washbowl, I jumped out the back doorframe onto the ground, kicked the fallen door where it lay, and for the first time in my life looked forward to polishing silver when I got home to impress the Kunkels the following evening.

CHAPTER

3

The dinner went off surprisingly well.

The Route 30 chickens were good, although they weren't fryers at all; they were six-pound roasting chickens cut in half. I've never learned to cut through joints, and Charles was too busy taking the storm windows off the front of the house to do it for me. So I left them as they were, serving only one vegetable to be sure they'd fit on the plates.

O. G. took on a lethal dose of martinis before dinner, swaying like a flagpole in a high wind as he helped himself from the buffet. Bob and Gil, the Chicago partners, drank right along with him, but they remained as solid as wooden Indians. Their precocious brains fed out figures on new stock issues, rediscount rates, and what might be expected from the reverse head and shoulders movement the stock market had assumed. They said, "Sir," every third word like a couple of platoon sergeants addressing their colonel.

Charles, at the head of the table, said nothing. I tried to shake him into verbal action by telepathy and a few quick jerks of my head, because I thought the others were stealing the scene, but he sat impassively cutting and eating his enormous chicken as if he had very little interest in the conversation.

When O. G. had the floor, he launched into a monologue on departmental procedures within the firm, terminating it only when Charles, putting down his knife and fork, announced he didn't agree with anything O. G. had said.

I managed to close my mouth which had fallen open in horrified astonishment, and tried to take comfort in O. G.'s obvious interest in Charles' counter opinions. He asked a lot of questions I didn't understand to which Charles replied with quiet deliberation. I couldn't tell if he was really brilliant or just plain stoned.

Maria and Jan, liberally bribed beforehand, wore clean dresses, passed the rolls, cleared the table, and brought in the ice cream with the chocolate cake I'd made in the middle of the night after cleaning the silver. I was so sleepy I forgot the baking powder so the cake was only about an inch high and heavy as lead, but I frosted it and cut it into squares.

"Ha!" O. G. exclaimed, helping himself, "Brownies! My favorite!"

Florence Harp, Maria's best friend, telephoned three times while we were at the table as she always does, but except for these interruptions things went smoothly.

After dinner we sat around the fire while Bernadine, O. G.'s Viking-like wife, draped in chiffon and covered with diamonds and lavender powder, regaled the women on the advantages of living in New York. New York was the *best* place in the world to buy clothes in spite of what people said about Paris and those new designers in California; New York had the most *marvelous* restaurants; the theater in New York was absolutely *marvelous,* and so on. Since almost our entire wardrobes were on our backs at that very moment and we had no hope of augmenting them, much less going to an expensive restaurant or buying theater tickets, Bernadine received small response.

Our attention turned to O. G. pouring whiskey and telling knock-knock jokes we'd all heard two years before. We laughed, yawned without opening our mouths, and stiffened our backs against the chairs so we wouldn't fall asleep.

The girls came in to say good-night (included in the bribe), curtsying clumsily in their patent leathers and trying not to giggle.

"Tell me, young lady," O. G. said to Maria, seizing her by the hand and pulling her to the side of his chair, "what have you been doing for fun lately?"

Maria swallowed, and attempted to disengage herself from his grasp. Finally she replied, "I had a neat time at Daddy's farm yesterday."

"Your daddy has a farm?"

"He just got it. It's in Indiana. He's going to raise cattle and hogs and Jan and I are going to sleep in a double-decker."

O. G.'s sunny countenance went under a cloud. He let go of Maria who escaped with Jan from the room. I heard their feet pounding up the stairs.

"Charles, you didn't mention to me that you had a farm. How do you plan to raise cattle in Indiana and continue the department program you outlined for me at Thurston, Dalton and Company?"

"No problem at all," Charles replied with a chest full of false confidence. "I have an experienced man at the farm so I don't have to do anything myself except run down there occasionally on Sundays."

"Don't you bring account work home with you to do over the weekends?" O. G. regarded Charles suspiciously.

"Certainly I do. I always complete it on Saturday night."

"Well," Mr. Kunkel continued, "I hope this farm won't prove to be a divided interest." Turning to his wife, he said, "Come, Bernadine, it's time we went back to town. Morning comes all too soon, and we want our sales force to be on their toes at the meeting." He gave Charles a sharp look.

After everyone had gone Charles made himself a double whiskey and soda, taking it to the chair O. G. had vacated.

32

"Of all the lousy, goddamned breaks!" he exploded. "We thought of everything except warning the kids to keep their mouths shut. How could Maria have spilled the beans? She's so antisocial she hardly ever says anything at all." He burrowed down in the cushion of his chair. "Gil will watch me like a hawk from now on waiting for me to turn up absent. If I do you may be sure he'll report it to O. G. How am I going to get the fields plowed, the corn in, the oats sown, if I don't go down there and build a fire under Art? He reads comic books all day in his kitchen if somebody doesn't get him moving. That's where I found him yesterday."

"Let's see now. After the meeting tomorrow there's not much coming up. Gil is going back to New York with O. G., so that's OK. We can go to the farm Tuesday and drive back early Wednesday morning."

"What are you going to do with your children? I seem to remember they go to school on Tuesdays."

"Get Millicent to come out for the night. She hasn't anything to do."

"All right, I'll call Millicent. It's eleven-thirty, but she has such bad insomnia she never sleeps anyway."

Millicent, Uncle Henry's only daughter, married a Milwaukee man, Ernest Krautter, who invented a soft drink called Push. A family background in the brewery business had made him a teetotaler, and at the wedding, which took place in the house in Kenwood, no alcohol could be served, not even the champagne Uncle Henry had laid down before Prohibition especially for this occasion. The punch was made of Push with gobs of raspberry ice floating around in it, and Uncle Henry was so outraged he never went to visit his daughter after her marriage in spite of her many invitations.

When Ernest Krautter died, Uncle Henry turned up at the funeral, which was in May, in linen golf knickers and a Norfolk jacket. He was dead drunk. It was the only time in the memory of the entire family he had done such a thing. He elected to sit in the rear of the church with the undertaker and the professional pallbearers whom he told in a loud voice throughout the service what robbers he thought they were.

At Uncle Henry's request, Millicent returned to Chicago to live splendidly in the Tudor mansion he bought for her on Wellington Avenue. Having no children, Millicent spent her affection on a farrago of dogs which romped throughout the elegant house, crowding at night into her Louis XV bed. She went to concerts, gave money to struggling artists, donated to the Chicago Art Museum a collection of jade miniatures, and had daily massages in a futile effort to keep her parfait-glass figure from spreading into the proportions of a brandy snifter. She was always lonely, and welcomed every opportunity to come to Charles' house for a visit with his family. Her own brothers, she said, were no good to her whatsoever. Stuffy Robert was practicing law in New York, and Henry, Jr., after failing in his endeavor to conduct an investment council service on the West Coast, had become an alcoholic. He was forever drying out in a pink stucco sanitorium, which didn't amuse her in the least.

Millicent had given us most of the furniture for our house and was enormously generous at Christmas. She spoiled Maria and Jan with an abundance of affection and elaborate but unsuitable presents, such as their gold rings set with diamonds and matching mink muffs to keep their hands warm while skating, which of course they never used.

Millicent answered the phone on the first ring. "Hello?" she said in a brisk voice.

"I didn't waken you, Millicent?"

"Good heavens, no, darling. I never sleep till four or five. I was just combing Peanuts, the Peke. He's gotten so woolly-looking lately. No silk to his coat at all. How's everybody? I've thought of you every moment since I heard Father left

34

Charles that dreadful farm. I'm so sorry. It was really quite mean of him. However are you going to manage?"

"That's what we're trying to figure out now." I relayed Charles' invitation.

"Of course I'll come! My little family has been house-bound for ages. How many may I bring?"

Millicent brought all eight of her dogs on her last visit. The harlequin Dane galloped playfully throughout the house, skidding the loose rugs in the front hall into a bundle against the wall, charging into tables, and knocking over chairs. When standing perfectly still he could remove glasses and ash trays from a table with two sweeps of his gay tail. The Dachshunds made olive green stains on the carpeting in the living room, and Peanuts, the Peke, had bitten the mailman, but what could I say?

"Bring them all if you like, Millicent."

"Oh, you're a dear! I'll have Stop and Shop put up a basket of wonders for the doggies, and don't order anything for me. I'm on yogurt again."

This was the first of numberless times Millicent stayed with the girls so Charles and I could go to the farm. When she became interested in the problems Charles was having in Indiana, she often joined us for the weekend, sleeping on a folding cot in the crowded living room in the capacious riding habit she'd bought to wear at the farm. She claimed that since she was up and prowling about most of the night there wasn't much use in getting undressed.

During one of her first visits she fell in love with a litter of Chester White pigs, and when she asked Charles if she could have one to take home with her, he couldn't refuse.

Millicent grew so fond of the piglet that she took it everywhere with her: to luncheons, to the old-fashioned grocery store she patronized on Broadway, and to the Friday symphonies where the pig slept through Saint-Saëns, Liszt, and Mozart, first in Millicent's small mink muff, then in the larger pillow-shaped beaver muff, and finally in the huge muff of Norwegian fox completely covering her lap as she sat in the concert hall listening to the music.

Her three Irish maids whose hairnets came right down to their eyebrows grudgingly helped her look after the pig, chasing him as he scampered across Aubusson rugs in an attempt to grab him before he could upset more treasures in the splendid drawing room. In spite of their efforts, Meissen lamps, Waterford candelabra, and bisque figurines crashed into fragments that had to be swept into a dustpan and carried out.

Alarmed by the increasing number of disasters and the fact that the pig had now grown too large to take out, Millicent consulted her hairdresser, Mr. Stan, on the future management of her pet.

I was at her house one morning when she shouted from under the hair dryer Mr. Stan brought with him, "I guess I can't keep the pig here any longer. If only I had a nice fenced yard, but Father didn't believe in yards. He said they just collected trash."

"We have a beautiful yard," said Mr. Stan who was almost as fond of the pig as Millicent. "Right in back of our apartment. Jon and I would adore having him." He looked appealingly at Millicent from under his auburn curls and bit off a fingernail. "Mayn't we have him?"

"Would you take good care of him and feed him properly?"

"But of course!" Mr. Stan cried, picking a sliver from the end of his tongue. "It would be so amusing to have a little pig living with us!"

"He's not so little any more," Millicent reminded him. "That's the trouble. He keeps bumping into things or pushing them over with his snout."

"He only needs more room. Oh, *do* let us have him!"

36

Millicent ducked her head out from under the dryer and looked at Mr. Stan. "Will you promise to telephone me frequently and tell me how he is?"

"Cross my heart and hope to die." The hairdresser drew an imaginery cross on the front of his perfectly tailored suit jacket.

The pig was stretched out along a tapestry settee. His eyes were closed, and every little while he grunted in his sleep as if he were dreaming.

Mr. Stan stroked the coarse white hair covering the pig's pink hide. "You're going to Stan and Jon's!" he cried.

The pig opened his eyes and buried his snout in the satin pillow on the end of the settee. Then he closed his eyes again.

"It's his nap time," Millicent observed.

"I'll wait until he wakes up," Mr. Stan whispered, pulling his double-jointed fingers until they cracked.

The first time Mr. Stan telephoned Millicent, he told her how much the pig was enjoying his new home. "He simply idolizes Jon!" he cried. "Jon made him a *quiche Lorraine* which he adored, especially the bacon part," he laughed gaily. "We've named him Billy Blue Fauntleroy. I hope that's all right with you."

The next time he called, he said, "Guess what?"

"What?" Millicent said.

"We're going to exhibit Billy Blue Fauntleroy in the livestock show! Jon thinks he'll win the blue ribbon. He's getting prettier every day. Thousands of people will see him. He's crazy about people, you know. I think we owe it to him, don't you?"

"Well," said Millicent.

"Please?"

"I suppose it's all right if you don't think it will make him nervous. Will there be lots of other pigs there?"

"Tons of them! But he'll be the most distinguished, I can

assure you. Jon has bought a book on how to groom pigs for a show. You'll never believe it, but after their bath they are sprinkled with talcum powder. It makes them whiter. You simply won't know him. Wait and see."

Millicent waited with misgivings, but when she saw her pig at the livestock show grown round and fat and white as a ghost, she was reassured. She looked fondly at Billy Blue Fauntleroy wearing a collar of flashing rhinestones around his fleshy neck, and smiled. Above his pen in the Amphitheatre hung a velvet banner on which his name was embroidered in gold thread.

As Mr. Stan predicted, thousands of people saw the pig. They stared at him and he stared right back. The press wrote columns about the hog raised in a city apartment by a firm of hairdressers. Did he have a chance of winning the blue ribbon in his class, competing as he would be against barrows fed and fitted for the show by some of the top hog breeders in the country? How was he going to stack up in the judging? Having been fed a continental diet, would his fleshing qualities appeal to the judges?

I stood behind Millicent, Mr. Stan, and Jon in the tanbark arena watching the judge inspect the class.

"He's superb, isn't he?" Jon whispered, but Mr. Stan was too occupied biting his nail to reply.

"It's a pity they wouldn't let him wear his collar," Millicent declared, "but clearly he's the best in the class anyway."

Almost as if the judge had heard her, he placed the blue ribbon across the sturdy white back of Billy Blue Fauntleroy, and the spectators responded with a round of applause.

The man who handled the pig for them in the class came up to Mr. Stan. "I'll let you know his auction number soon as the committee gives it to me," he said.

"Auction number?" The three faces regarded him in bewilderment.

"His number for the packers' sale. You want to know how he dresses out, don't you?"

Millicent gasped.

"See here, my good man," Jon began, but he was interrupted by a dull thud. Mr. Stan had keeled over onto the tanbark.

Pulling herself together Millicent instructed the handler to guide Billy Blue Fauntleroy with the end of his flicking whip to her waiting limousine. With difficulty her chauffeur and the handler hoisted him in the back seat onto the velour cushions beside Millicent who buckled on his collar. With the rhinestones flashing sparks in the bright sunshine he looked out the window as the long black car snaked through the traffic at the stockyards.

Back at her house Millicent put the pig in the largest of her bedrooms, the blue guest suite called the Wedgewood Room. There he remained until Charles persuaded her to return him to the farm. "He'll be much happier," he told her.

Only when Charles promised on his word of honor he would never send the pig to market did Millicent agree, reluctantly, to part again with her pet.

For a long time Billy Blue Fauntleroy was the only animal of note on the farm. He had many visitors, and when Charles was invited to bring him to the county fair as a special exhibit one autumn he commanded a great deal of attention, surveying his surroundings from the confines of an over-sized pen with an urbane and experienced eye.

CHAPTER
4

Inspired by Charles' weekend pep talks, Art's childlike face puckered thoughtfully as he listened to the outlined plans. Charles hired another man, Enoch Ordway, a taciturn fellow who batched it with his skinny hound dog on the Schlagers' third floor. With the addition of a secondhand tractor on which Charles took his turn, the fields got plowed, the oats sown, the corn planted.

The twin silos Uncle Henry had built were still empty, but the anticipation of filling them with succulent green silage at the end of the summer kept a glimmer of encouragement in Charles' red-rimmed eyes. During the weekly drives back to town he talked of future plans and improvements, all the while scratching his body inflamed by the itch dirt from the blowing black sand in the fields, and gouging his belt line measled by chigger bites. Oliver and his infected harem were replaced by a herd of purebred Aberdeen Angus cows with calves at side supposedly bred back to an Illinois bull, Blackcap Buster. Charles bought the cows sight unseen, admitting he wouldn't have known what he was looking for if he had gone to the Indiana auction himself instead of sending Art and Enoch.

The fifty head of steers he bought over the telephone from a broker at the stockyards in Chicago and had shipped down to the farm stood up to the bunks in the feedlot, eating the corn we had to buy from the grain elevator in Zulu.

The central hog house at the back of the Schlagers' was

40

remodeled and filled with sows due to farrow in midsummer, which proved disastrous, but for the moment we felt we were in business.

Inside, things did not progress as well. The house was a lot smaller to live in than to look at. "There are only four of us," Charles remarked, "but I feel like that circus act where thirty clowns climb out of a two-seater automobile. It's not only crowded; there isn't any place to put things."

The girls' double-decker proved a valuable space saver in the former dining room, even though Maria in the upper bunk suffered a little. She had to flatten herself and ease into bed sideways from the top of the ladder, for there wasn't enough headroom for her to crawl into it. Watching her go to bed reminded me of trying to slide a plump envelope into a very shallow drawer.

"Just don't try to turn over," Jan commented in answer to Maria's complaints, "and you'll be all right."

"I can't sleep on my back *all* the time!" Maria exclaimed indignantly. "It's not good for my posture, and besides sleeping on your back makes you dream. Miss Grube told us that in hygiene."

"Be quiet!" Charles snapped from our room where we were lying practically on top of one another in the pit of the thin mattress spread across a gorge in the middle of the sagging springs. If we altered our positions or attempted to turn over, the movement loosened the brass knobs which fell off the bedstead and rolled around interminably on the bare floor.

It was several days before Charles refrained from peeling off his socks at night and throwing them on the kitchen table which was already set for breakfast. By mutual agreement a ten-cent penalty was imposed on anyone leaving any article of clothing where it could be seen. We used the wardrobe in the living room for our things. Maria kept hers in a cardboard carton in a corner of the former dining room. Jan simply folded her clothes neatly under her mattress. The Navy would have been proud of us.

The supply of water during those first days at the farm was the most annoying problem. The pipes, clogged with sand and badly in need of repair, grudgingly emitted treacherous-looking trickles which I collected and boiled. But at the end of a few weeks the four-room cottage was becoming more livable. With the help of the plumber from Zulu, Art, and his wife, Lottie, we made giant strides. We had a new mattress which lessened the depth of the gully in the bed; we had a new back door, back steps, unbroken window panes, and an adequate supply of running water. We had to use the old wardrobe, the heating stove in the living room, and the velour chair bleeding stuffing on the linoleum rug, but we had a brand-new kitchen stove to replace the old one that blew up in my face.

Some women can walk up to any old stove, stare it in the face, light it, and extract from it a perfect performance, whereas I approach an unfamiliar stove with great caution and a lighted match held at arm's length, expecting the worst and usually getting it.

I was cowering in the corner in the blackened shreds of what had been a dutiful flannel robe when Art, summoned from the fields by the Jovian blast, burst through the kitchen door.

"It's them crappy oryfices," he commented, turning off the flow of gas that smelled of rotten onions. "This here stove, it's always done like that. Ronnie, the fellow looked after them chickens, he made it hisself outen old parts and hooked her up to the bottled gas, but he put in the plates that had ought to be in a natural gas stove. Them holes is too big for bottled gas."

He regarded me solemnly with his pale, unblinking

eyes. "You ain't hurt none? You look kinda baldlike with no hair, or nuthin!" Folding his muscular arms across his chest he slouched against the kitchen wall. "You know that Ronnie, he was an odd one. Always moonying around. I and her has always said he was moony-like on account of his kid was one of them wharfs. Never did get but two, three foot high." Art gossiped companionably until it was too dark to return to the fields.

After he left I turned on the lights provided by our own electric plant, an atavistic monster called The Bowers, berthed in a shed on a nearby dune. Reluctantly the lamps cast a faltering path of light across the linoleum rugs, but if we plugged in an iron or a radio, something was certain to blow, and we spent the evening pumping up gasoline lamps, or sitting in total darkness. REA had not yet discovered Muskrat County.

We filled the ancient wooden icebox on the back porch with the block of ice we brought down from Winnetka. We learned that if we bought a hundred-pound block, about fifty pounds would melt on the way down, and the remaining fifty was the exact amount the box would accommodate. When we didn't forget to empty the drip pan underneath, it worked very well.

The first time I saw Lottie Schlager, I was hanging the new curtains at the window in the kitchen. She came plowing through the sand from her house to ours followed by a swarm of children. It was a raw windy day, and Lottie was wearing one of Art's checkered woolen shirts over her cotton housedress. Her hair above her round rosy face was skewered with bobby pins, and as she labored through the sand I saw that on her bare feet she had an old pair of Art's shoes, laceless, with the tongues flapping.

"Anybody to home?" she roared in a Wagnerian bass.

I stepped out on the back porch; at the sight of me the

children drew close to their mother, the littlest ones hiding behind her.

"How are youse gittin' along?" She inquired. "Anything we'uns can do for you folks?"

I invited her in, but she shook her head and laughed.

"Ain't hardly enough room inside for the mess of us-uns."

When I asked the names of her children she lined them up with pride. "This here is Junior. He's the oldest. Then come Martha, Ada, Ruth, and Esther. Next is Milbert." She laid a hand on top of her little boy's head. "He ain't but three. This here last one is Crystal." She picked up a grimy, runny-nosed toddler and held her in her arms. "I was aimin' to call the girls after the points of the Star," she explained, "but when Milbert, he come along, I got mixed up on account he was a boy. I'd plum forgot the last point, bein's I couldn't keep up with the lodge meetings in town, so I called her Crystal, and you know, she wasn't half dry from the Reverend's sprinkle when I remembered the name, Electa. Ain't it a pity?"

Lottie looked lovingly at the baby's face whose large expressionless eyes were set far apart beneath wisps of brown hair spread across her tiny forehead. "She ain't bright like the others," she remarked. "A person don't know what ails her. One day I reckon I'll take her in town to see old Doc Gibbs." Lowering her eyes she spoke as softly as her strident voice permitted. "You don't reckon the good Lord, He left something outen her on account I didn't finish the points of the star?"

"Of course not. Whatever it is she'll probably outgrow it."

"That's jest what I been tellin' myself. Now you young-uns, git!" She waved her arms as if she were shooing chickens, and the older children scampered back to the

44

house. "I expect a person could use another pair of hands inside," she declared, propping Crystal up in a sand-filled corner of the back porch. "Settlin' is a mite wearyin'."

Lottie's kindness, remarkable strength, and great patience were inspirational during those weeks when I discovered I was inept, ignorant, and totally unprepared to live on a farm. Both thumbs were darkened by hammer blows; my back ached because I'd never learned to lift with my arms; my face and hands were a collage of paint, mortar, putty, and wallpaper paste.

Charles fared better. He seemed as much at home setting a new fencepost as he was in the board room at his office.

I took strength watching Lottie go about her chores, chopping up oak wood for her stove, or skillfully splintering the shingles fallen from the siding of her house into a fireworks of fine kindling. I observed her with admiration striding through the sand, a feed sack slung over one shoulder, to tend her chickens, or with a pail in either hand setting out to slop the hogs she kept to feed her family. She stood at the hog trough shouting into the wind, "Suck, suck, suck, suck, suck, suck, ho − −eeey!" Her voice ricocheted off the dunes, but the hogs got the message and galloped up to the trough into which she flung the liquid contents of her pails.

She taught me "the signs" by which she conducted her life: what a person should do or shouldn't do in the dark of the moon; that a person should never kill a chicken by chopping off its head and letting the bird bleed − he should step on the chicken's neck and twist its head off; if a housewife baked a cake when she had her monthly the cake was "bounden" to fall.

She taught me how to crank the battery telephone on the kitchen wall, at the same time identifying some of the voices we heard as we listened on the party line. "That's Gump

Childers. Him and his two brothers lives a piece down the road with Blue Burnett, and a dirtier lot a person won't never see. Them boys races roaches of an evening acrost their kitchen table when they ain't playin' cards."

I heard the Hill sisters, the paperhangers in Zulu, contracting to repaper the parlor of Doc Stiles, the vet, who at eighty did his work without an assistant. I heard Ma Hollenstetter, the Amish woman who farmed near Othie Struber's sawmill, telling 'Tater Bug Miller at the hardware store to lay aside a drum of axle grease for her. "Them Amishers," Lottie explained, "they farm with horses, and of a Saturday night they drive to town in a spring wagon with beards blowin' and bonnets flappin' to do their week's tradin'. Their religion, it don't let them folks use nuthin' with a motor in it. Ain't that a caution?"

Lottie was kind to Maria and Jan when they were at the farm, giving them freshly baked bread spread with apple butter made from the wormy apples in Uncle Henry's orchard, forgotten now in the thrust for greater economic yield, but it was Art who captivated the girls, especially Maria.

Maria was at his side all day long, handing him a grease gun if he was working in the machine shed, carrying a pair of wire cutters as she rode behind him on the tractor into the pastures to mend fences, or wielding a second scoop when Art dug the caked manure from the floor of the old barn.

Jan stayed with them for awhile, but her greatest pleasure was putting a work bridle on Old Mae, a pensioned Morgan mare, and riding bareback through the woods where she found, or invented, enchanted vales that fired her imagination and that of her mythical mentors, Miss Pearl and Miss Diamond.

The girls sensed in Art and in his family a less conventional and therefore more appealing way of life than their own. They began to imitate him. They slouched around the

46

way he did; they scratched their chests with their thumb-
nails; they spoke in his idiom. At supper one evening when
we were fitting ourselves around the oilcloth-covered table in
the small kitchen, Maria said, "Daddy why can't *we* have an
outdoor shithouse like Uncle Art's?"

CHAPTER
5

We went into summer with the feeling that all was well with the farm. At least Charles did.

"We've made a start, a real good one," he declared. "The oats look all right to me; the cows seem happy enough even though our grass isn't as thick as the grass in the photographs in last month's Ag bulletin. It says the fields should be limed. We'll probably have to do that next year."

We were setting a new corner post for the Cant-Sag gate at the entrance to the farm. Charles was jabbing the posthole digger in the earth instructing me at the same time in the art of making concrete from a bag of cement, sand scooped up from the ground, and gravel from the county road. We had brought along a drum of water on the wagon box behind the tractor.

"The corn reminds me of the narcissus bulbs we used to grow in a dish when we were kids," I told Charles. "Only about every fourth one came out."

"I know what you mean, Mary. The corn doesn't look up to par. It could be the fertilizer. Maybe we haven't put on enough, or maybe we haven't used the right kind."

I recalled the conversation between Art and Charles when they were discussing fertilizer one evening at the kitchen table. Art said he believed 0-20-20 was what we needed, and Charles countered with 0-12-12 which was recommended in the bulletin.

"Oh," said Art, "I don't expect a person needs two

kinds." He got up, stretched, and announced he was going home, "bein's Lottie brought back a stacka new comics from town," and he was mighty anxious to read what "Little Orkin Annie" was up to.

"Anyway," Charles commented, "we can't do everything at once. Learning to farm properly takes time." He removed his hat, wiped his suntanned face with his gloved hand, and leaned for a moment on the handles of the posthole digger, shiny from long use.

"It's gratifying to see the result of our efforts in such a short time, but we still have a long way to go. We've got to think about the buildings. They need a lot of repairs even though Uncle Henry had new foundations put under some of them."

"Don't you miss playing tennis?" I was stirring the concrete with an old ax handle.

"Not especially."

I thought of the Saturday afternoon games we'd had on the Winnetka public courts, the cold drinks afterward, dinner with our tennis group. I sighed. "Well, tennis doesn't cost as much as farming. I saw the feed bills from the grain elevator. They're colossal. I don't see how we can pay them."

"The bank isn't worried. The loan department thinks we could have a good thing going down here."

Charles poured the mixture into the hole he'd dug, and together we set the post. "Anyway, what can I do? We're stuck with this place, and in my judgment the only thing to do is try to make it pay. Maybe one day someone will come along and make us an offer for it, but until that happens we've got to do the best we can with it ourselves."

"If someone did offer to buy it," I persisted, "would you sell it?"

Charles hesitated a moment before answering.

"I suppose so. I'm willing to admit it interests me, and

I'd like very much to be able to build the farm into a paying operation, but common sense tells me with the limited time I can spend on it, and having to drag the kids down every weekend, it isn't going to be easy. I suppose I would sell it, to answer your question."

In August all previous heat records were broken. The pastures assumed the appearance of burned waffles, and the chinch bugs in red and black battalions were devouring the corn with the enthusiasm of a radio commercial for breakfast food. Every sow on the place farrowed on the same day when the thermometer stood at 110 degrees. There had not been a drop of rain in thirty days and the drought looked as if it would last another thirty. Every night the sun, a huge overripe tomato, went down in a cloudless sky.

Charles was in New York with Gil and Bob to attend a meeting before O. G. and his Viking sailed on the *Normandie* for a summer holiday.

Maria had been invited to spend two weeks with Florence Harp at the Harp's summer place in Wisconsin, and Jan who had developed an exaggerated fondness for horses was at a dude ranch in Wyoming with Millicent to improve her riding while Millicent played poker with the cowboys.

I was alone at the farm.

"Them sows is gobblin' up their pigs fast as they pop out," Art reported one morning when I came out of the house at seven-thirty. He took off his straw hat, holding it against the striped bib of his overalls while he mopped his steaming face with the sleeve of his work shirt. "We-uns'll have to set them sows and litters in A houses under the trees so's they can git some air. They can't hardly breathe in that hog barn he fixed up."

Art and Enoch threw the individual houses on a wagon behind the M, unloading them under the ragged water oaks whose limp dusty leaves hung in the dead air without a flutter.

50

"It's a mighty good thing we got these here piss oaks," Art observed, finishing the last wire pen outside the houses. "It's the only shade on the whole place."

Grunting complaints, the sows were moved to their new quarters. Art filled some buttermilk barrels with water and hauled them to the pens. "We'll slop 'em real good first," he instructed, "and then we-uns'll jest slosh 'em off with the rest of the water."

Standing on the wagon box, Art and I dipped water from the barrels and threw it over the sweltering sows while Enoch returned to the well house where he'd been trying to coax the pump into action. It had broken a part, and he was attempting to repair it with a piece of baling wire. The blades of the windmills seemed rusted to the hot sky. We were almost out of water.

"We ain't goin' to have hardly more'n one or two pigs to the litter," Art announced pessimistically. "A person needs to average six to break even."

We sloshed with renewed vigor.

At exactly twelve o'clock Art put down his pail and eased himself off the wagon box. "Reckon I won't git nuthin' for my dinner that tastes as good to me as them pigs does to them sows. I betcha them pigs is sweeter than squirrel meat." He sauntered off toward his house while I continued to pour water over the distressed sows.

If I stopped to rest my back a few minutes, the sows got hot again and resumed their cannibalistic carnival. It seemed they were running a contest to see who could eat the most piglets in the least amount of time. Finally the barrels were empty.

Sick and frustrated I started toward the cottage. Halfway there I saw a car drive up the lane and shiver to a stop in the barnlot where the heat rose from the sand in dizzying spirals against the barn.

There was little likelihood Art would leave his house

until he'd finished his dinner and his nooning, so I detoured to the barnlot.

A man in a suit was getting out of the car. It was a rare occurrence when someone came to the farm wearing anything but overalls. A country suit from a small-town haberdashery lent an air of importance to the wearer.

The man told me he was the regional director of the Aberdeen Angus Association; he'd heard we had bought some purebred cows, and he wanted to make our acquaintance and inquire if he might be helpful to us in any way. He handed me a card.

"My husband is in New York, Mr. Hardy, but would you like to see the cows?"

"I'd be delighted!" He took off his suit jacket and folded it carefully across the seat of the car before following me through the sand to the barn where the cows had flattened themselves under the overhang for refuge from the broiling sun.

"These are the mother cows?" Mr. Hardy seemed surprised.

"They look more like grandmothers, don't they?" I hadn't realized how skinny they were.

"Hmm," said Mr. Hardy, regarding the sad-eyed beasts.

"We've weaned their calves and are waiting for the new ones to come, but so far nothing has happened."

"You bought them with calves at side and rebred?"

"That's right."

"Hmm," said Mr. Hardy again, and squatted down to examine the cows' bags.

"What's the matter?"

"I don't believe these matrons are with calf," he declared. "Pity."

"But they were bred to Blackcap Buster," I told him, "in Illinois."

52

"Sometimes it doesn't take."

"What doesn't take?"

"The cover."

"What's a cover?"

He flushed. "The service of the bull."

"You mean we won't have any calf crop this year?"

"It doesn't look like it to me. If I were you, I'd get a bull to run with the cows. That way you'd be sure. Also, I'd increase the ration of these cows. They're not getting enough to eat."

"They're eating grass. We've left the gates open so they can graze all the pastures if they want to."

Mr. Hardy rolled his eyes over the burned fields and shrugged his narrow shoulders. "Usually supplemental feed isn't necessary this time of the year," he explained, "but with the drought and the condition of the grass you'll have to supplement."

The Schlagers' screen door banged, and Art came sliding down his dune with a toothpick stuck between his two front teeth.

"Mr. Hardy doesn't think the cows are getting enough to eat," I said, after introducing the men.

"I was just saying," Mr. Hardy remarked to Art, "that I thought the mother cows should have some supplemental feed."

Art lost his toothpick to the sand in a redundant belch.

"Now the steers look good." Mr. Hardy swung over the fence into the adjacent feedlot and stood behind the black cattle lined up at a bunk eating ground corn covered with blackstrap molasses swarming with flies. "You wouldn't have to put as much in the mother cows, of course."

"If I was you, mister," Art called, "I wouldn't stand behind them steers. I seen 'em shit twenty feet a time or two."

Mr. Hardy took a quick step backward.

"Mr. Hardy," I said, "I was just going into the house for lunch when you arrived. Wouldn't you like a sandwich or something?" I'd been told that in the country if anyone stopped in at mealtime you were obliged to invite him to eat with you.

"Why, thank you. That's very kind." He plowed steadfastly behind me up the sand hill to the cottage.

The moment I stepped into the kitchen I remembered I hadn't been to town for groceries for several days. There was no meat, no milk, no butter, no bread, not even a Kool-Aid in the ice box. Well, there was bound to be something in the kitchen cabinet. Opening the door I stared in disbelief at its entire contents: two cans of chili con carne and a squashed box of Kleenex.

Opening the cans I wondered briefly if anyone had ever eaten cold chili. On such a hot day almost anything would be more agreeable unheated, but when I scraped the lumps of meat and mashed beans from the can into the bowls the sight gagged me. Reluctantly I reached for a saucepan.

While I was in the kitchen Mr. Hardy sat patiently in the blue velour living room chair, humming contentedly to himself in rightful expectation of a good midday dinner.

I hated to disturb the image of fried chicken, mashed potatoes, homemade pickles, and apple pie in his mind, but what could I do? Putting the two bowls on the table, I called him into the kitchen.

"I wonder if I could have a glass of water?" Mr. Hardy, seated across the table from me, was gallantly spooning in the steaming chili.

"Of course!" I took a glass from the shelf above the sink and turned on the faucet.

No water.

"We've run out again, I guess," I said, feeling sorry for

the sad-faced little man who had tried to be helpful. "The hogs had what was left in the tank this morning and the pump's broken."

Mr. Hardy appeared on the verge of tears. Sweat blistered on his bald head; his pink torso shone through his wet white shirt. "Never mind," he said politely. "I must be going along." Rising from the table he shook my hand, turned, and walked into three streamers of flypaper swinging from the ceiling.

After Mr. Hardy had gone I went down to the well house where Enoch was finishing his makeshift job of repairing the pump with baling wire. "She's good as new," he said, listening to the uncertain throbs under the floor. "Now we gotta do something about them chinch bugs, else we ain't goin' to have no corn crop at all."

He put a bridle and collar on Old Mae and, chaining a log to the traces, walked behind the mare up and down the rows of corn. He hung a drum of creosote around my neck, instructing me to follow him and fill the trench made by the log. "Only hope we have of killing them little bastards," he commented, his jaw stuffed with wintergreen snuff.

At the end of two hours in the searing sun I began to see large black spots. My legs weighed a hundred pounds apiece and my shoulders felt as if they had slipped down around my knees. Leaving Enoch with an apology I staggered back from the fields up to the dune where the sows were. Art was still soaking them. They had stopped eating their pigs; instead they were rolling on them in a kind of sybaritic abandon.

Everything was against us, I thought in despair. Nature, a lack of physical strength, knowledge, even Art and Enoch. Why couldn't *they* do something? They'd both grown up on this poisonous land. Why hadn't they learned something about it?

The sun was going down in slow motion beyond the ditch

bank as I walked back to the house. I was too tired to eat even if there had been anything in the kitchen. I sat down on the back steps, wishing a breeze would stir the quiet, dust-laden leaves of the oak tree overhead. The thermometer had dropped to ninety-eight, but it always seemed hotter at dusk than in the middle of the day. In the twilight sky, heat lightning forked over the parched fields as usual, but I'd given up hope for a storm to clear the air and bring rain.

"I'll declare it's a scary thing when a person sees them kildeers flyin' like that and it don't rain." It was Lottie coming toward the cottage carrying a brown crock and a pitcher. "Most times when them birds dives and circles close to the ground of an evening it's bounden to rain, but they been doin' it now for weeks, and we ain't had a drop." She sat down beside me on the steps. "I toted over a mess of beans and some lemonade. You ain't been off the place for the best part of a week, and I figured you might be runnin' a little close in the kitchen."

All at once my appetite returned. I got a plate and heaped it with the beans Lottie had baked, swilling down the lemonade with the eagerness of a Bedouin on the desert. It tasted better than Christmas dinner. Between mouthfuls I thanked Lottie. She laughed and said it wasn't all that tasty; it "jest slipped down good" on account my "stummick had most growed together from not eatin'."

"But you know," she went on, "he always liked them beans, too."

"Who?"

"The old man. Him he calls "Uncle Henry." I'd tote down a pot now and again to his house and he'd clean it up neat as a hound dog. He told me a bean pot put him in mind of all the good and proper things there was in life. He said when he was a young-un in the East, his ma, she give her kids a pot of beans of a Saturday night after the Bible readin'.

He said since he'd growed up he ain't never had nuthin' as good. And him with money enough to buy anything he wanted! Looked like he never hankered after nuthin' for hisself. Sure as God he was satisfied with them beans. They was some kind of a sign to that old man, I reckon."

After Lottie left I thought about what she'd said. It was true that Uncle Henry didn't hanker after anything. He'd always had everything he wanted. His houses and automobiles he took for granted as suitable shelter and transportation for himself and his family, but I couldn't remember him ever indulging himself in a personal extravagance. He hated "show" and four-flushing. He was disgusted with his children when they were growing up and insisted on having silly things such as class rings and college ties. He lectured them regularly about the foolish ways they spent their allowances.

Uncle Henry performed his parental duties as he saw fit, giving his children a good home, a good education, and the opportunity of continuing the business he had built up. The fact that the boys refused this opportunity must have been the greatest bewilderment in his life.

"Nothing but a bunch of milksops!" He shouted at them, as one by one they turned away from the rough-and-tumble competition of his construction business to quieter and more refined pursuits. He must have been terribly disappointed.

His business was Uncle Henry's whole life; he trained for it as an athlete trains for the Olympic Games. Only after he sold it did he turn his hand to other things, the little things men grasp at when they find themselves floundering in a sea of too much time.

He set up a workshop in the basement of his house in Kenwood where he constructed a variety of monstrous failures. He built a mission couch, an enormous oaken thing he covered with brown leather, designed for his side porch overlooking a bed of lilies of the valley, his favorite flower. But he failed to measure the upstairs door so the piece of furniture never reached its destination.

When he recovered from the depression his error cast upon him, he built a sled for Maria, who was hardly more than a baby. He used the stoutest oak wood he could find and he secured the back and sides with bolts large enough to support a beam in a factory ceiling. Instead of rope, he inserted a loop of steel cable in the steering arm. When at last the sled was finished it was too heavy to pull.

Abandoning the basement shop he went to his summer home in Rollingwood, a suburb south of Chicago, where he decided to take up golf. Those of his friends who weren't dead played golf, so why shouldn't he? He signed up for lessons with the professional, appearing every morning on the practice tee at seven-thirty. He wound up in a mighty swing, took a heroic swipe at the ball which, if it moved at all, merely skittered off the tee into the clumps of long grass surrounding it. Blowing like a porpoise, he teed up another, and another, until the bucket of balls was empty. Then he argued with the pro. He had special clubs made with extra large faces, and hacked around the course by himself, his face empurpled more from anger than the sun.

When the pater-filius tournament came up at the end of the summer, he felt he had a chance to win it. For his partner he chose Charles, whose handicap was ten strokes higher than that of his own sons. With his linen plus fours ballooning around his legs in a stiff wind, he teed off in front of the gallery. The ball started off straight enough, and for a moment it looked as if his shot would be down the fairway, but then as usual, it sliced off in an arc to the right and like a boomerang started coming back to him. Charles addressed the ball for his alternate shot, and laid it in a trap to the left of the green. By the time the gallery arranged themselves around the trap, Uncle Henry was chopping furiously with

58

his mashie-niblick raising bursts of sand but not moving the ball. He swung again and again, until finally a voice in the gallery called out, "Let the boy have a turn, Henry."

After the tournament (won by the club member Uncle Henry disliked the most and his son who was only ten years old), he practiced harder than ever, but nothing seemed to improve him. Finally he gave up golf and bought an ex-cavalry horse for fifty dollars, claiming riding was better exercise than golf anyway.

He rode through the bridle trails of Washington Park at a dead gallop, a cigar clenched between his teeth, his stocky legs wrapped in World War I khaki puttees. There was in the park a statue which must have been especially offensive to the horse, for each time he raced by it he shied, ducking out from under Uncle Henry who kept going in a straight line until eventually he hit the ground. Finally he learned to avoid the loop of the trail where the statue stood.

Perhaps his greatest achievement other than business was making wine which he would never have thought of if he hadn't gone on one of his infrequent visits to Paris to see Cousin Will Webb.

In addition to his interest in music and the arts and his remarkable knowledge of French history, Cousin Will was a connoisseur of wines.

"It takes him half an hour to down one small glass of the stuff," Uncle Henry wrote back, but he got some sort of message from the experience. On his return he decided to make wine from the vineyards in back of the garden at his house in Rollingwood.

He instructed Ernst, his gardener, to get the vines in shape. Together they picked the grapes, mashed them in a vat, put them through a press, added water and sugar, and poured the juice into five-gallon jugs which they hauled into his town house to be stored in the basement.

When Uncle Henry thought the juice was sufficiently

fermented he removed the corks he had tied on, and let the jars stand open until the gas escaped before siphoning the liquid into empty Apollinaris bottles he had saved for this purpose. Capping the bottles with metal tops, he laid them down on the racks built of discarded templates, soft pine lumber used as forms for marking rivet holes which over the years he'd brought home from his shop in Pullman, insisting that one day he would find some use for them. The bottles remained in the template racks for six months, a year, and sometimes two years, depending on when Uncle Henry thought the wine was properly aged.

Scarcely a night went by without an explosion in the basement. The losses were great, but when the wine was brought to the table Uncle Henry, beaming with pleasure, forgot the losses. His delight carried with it, however, a few surprises. Because of the ripeness of the grapes, or the greenness, too much sugar, or too little, and the variety of the grapes themselves, he never knew whether he was going to open a rosé, a rich burgundy, a sparkling white wine, or an undrinkable dud. When he had company he sometimes had to open several bottles before he found the kind of wine he'd promised his guests.

Nothing but his business really worked for Uncle Henry. Why then had he bought a farm? And why had he left it to Charles? There had to be some explanation.

He would not have approved of the way things were going. There would be no crops, no calves, not enough pigs to defray the cost of feeding the sows. We were in debt to the bank. We had worked hard, read books, tried everything we knew to pull things together into a plausible economy; I doubted he could have done any better.

Perhaps he had plans for the farm we didn't know about. Had he made some outline for a plan of operating the place that we hadn't found? Or was he considering using it for pleasure as a kind of shooting and fishing establishment? It seemed unlikely, in spite of Art telling Charles how Uncle Henry used to go out with him when he checked his muskrat traps along the ditch bank; how he'd walk all day long through the wet smart weed in the fall, gun in hand, hoping for a shot at a cock pheasant; and how, in the summer, the old man lay on his stomach alongside of Art on the plank bridge across the ditch bank, his drop line baited with dough balls Lottie had made, patiently waiting for a catch of slimy bullheads.

If he had any program in mind to make the farm pay, it was lost to us. Maybe there was a clue among his files in the old running board trunk stored with his stuffed tarpon in the Schlagers' attic. When it was cooler I would suggest to Charles that he have a look at those files.

Wearily I got up from the steps and went inside the house. The Bowers was in one of its fluctuating moods. The lamps alternately faltered to the dimmest beacon and then brightened to a frightening glare in measured cadence like someone breathing.

I lay on the bed with the new book, *Gone with the Wind*, which I'd waited weeks to get at the rental library in Winnetka. I was deeply engrossed in the battle of Atlanta when the lights failed altogether. I closed my eyes, hoping they would come on again, which they sometimes did. I never knew whether they did, or didn't, for I fell into a dead man's sleep from which I was awakened by a tremendous boom. My first thought was of the cannons on Peachtree Street. I sprang out of bed into a blinding glare accompanied by a simultaneous explosion that split my ears. Three more flashes and booms followed in terrifying succession. Outside there was a muffled sound like someone beating rugs. When I ran to the window I saw a wall of water falling and the sky was illuminated by continuing flashes of lightning. The dusty sand absorbed the rain, deadening its sound.

I closed the window and was on the point of hopping

back in bed when three golden spheres as large as beach balls bounced along the wire leading from The Bowers house to ours. My feet refused to move. I shut my eyes, and stuffed my fingers in my ears. There was one jolt that knocked me to the floor, another explosion of thunder, and then with a fearsome hiss a ribbon of fire snaked along the baseboards to which we'd stapled cords and extension wires. Lamps jumped off their tables. The telephone, shooting flames like a dragon, rang wildly.

In a second it was over. Why the house didn't go up in flames I cannot explain. The extent of the damage appeared to be only a charred rut along the baseboards and six broken lamp bulbs. The telephone receiver had been blown off its hook and was wagging back and forth on its cord like a long black tongue.

"That sure was a goose-drownder we had last night," Art remarked in the morning. "Three of them piss oaks by the powerhouse was struck clean off their trunks, but we could stand a heap more rain."

The ground was still dusty. It was difficult to believe it had rained at all. The sun was out, hot as ever, and the pale sky was as cloudless as it had been for a month.

"How are the sows?"

"Them sows is wallerin' happy as bears. They ain't eatin' no more pigs, neither. Enoch, he's got the pump workin' fine, and the tank, it's full to the top. I declare, though, that thunder scares a person. I and her lay with a quilt over our heads the whole night through. I seen them thunder-pumpers flappin' their wings on the ditch bank yesterday evening, but I sure didn't know they was aimin' to pump up nuthin' like we got."

With a full tank of water I decided I could have a bath before driving to Chicago to meet Charles coming in from New York on the Commodore Vanderbilt.

While soaking the dirt off in the oak-rimmed tub, I thought how pleasant it would be to return to our house in Winnetka. The house would need a cleaning, and we'd have to mow the lawn and weed the flower bed, but once those things were done we could go to the country club on Millicent's guest card to play tennis, swim in the pool, and drink rum punches with lots and lots of ice in them. We'd have some friends in for dinner, and I wouldn't have to yell at the kids to make their beds and pick up their rooms, for they were still away.

The car shuddered through the sand in the barnlot and raised a cloud of black cinders in the lane and a film of powdery white dust on the gravel road as I sped happily for the highway leaving behind me the farm and its impossible problems.

My respite was short. At the station in Chicago, Charles barely kissed me before he said, "Let's drive right down to the farm. I can't wait to get there!"

Turning around, we headed back to Zulu.

CHAPTER
6

For a week we fought the chinch bugs, taking turns from sunup to sundown dragging the log and filling the trenches with creosote in a desperate effort to halt the destruction of the corn plants. It was hopeless. The chinch bugs worked day *and* night. Every morning there was further discouraging evidence of their voracious nocturnal appetites. They had us and they knew it.

Three of our twenty sows died in spite of Charles buying several long hoses, putting them together, and connecting them to a hydrant in the vacated hog house so that whoever wasn't annihilating chinch bugs trained a steady stream of water on the sows gasping in their pens.

Farming seemed to be an eternal struggle to destroy life on one hand, and to preserve it on the other.

"Ain't he bright to have thought this up?" Art commented to me approvingly as he screwed the brass end of the hose on the tap. "This here hydrogen, it's been lookin' right at us, but ain't a one of us thought about all them hoses. He ain't got no marbles in his head, I betcha."

"He's smart, all right," I agreed wearily.

Shortly before noon the truckload of feeder steers arrived from the West that Charles had bought through his livestock broker. He got them at a bargain price, he said, because the grass had dried up on the plains.

"We kin unload them steers in this here pen close to the barnlot so's you won't git your wheels stuck in the sand," Art told the driver. "Jest open your tailgate and we'll jump 'em off."

But when the tailgate was removed we saw a pile of prostrated animals too weak to stand up, let alone jump.

The men dragged them out, one at a time. About every third one was able to wobble over to the water trough in the pen. The others were dead or dying.

The driver claimed he'd unloaded them to rest them, and had given them water and feed, and maybe he did. He looked little better than his cargo. "Hell can't be no hotter than them oiled roads in Kansas," he said as he followed Art up to his house to piece on the cold lunch meats and iced tea Lottie had put out. She had taken the kids to visit Ma Hollenstetter, the Amish woman, who had been gored by her bull in a field and was, Lottie informed us, "leakin' blood somethin' awful."

Enoch returned to the well house with more baling wire (the pump had broken down again), and Charles and I went to our house to eat the chicken salad I'd made and left in a bowl inside another bowl of cold water. (The ice we'd brought back from the city had melted two days before.) The salad had spoiled, so we had to have peanut butter sandwiches again and lukewarm Kool-Aids.

"Someday we'll get electricity here," Charles said, patting my arm, "and then we can have a refrigerator with ice cubes and everything. It isn't fair to subject you to this kind of living. I'm awfully sorry about it."

Charles had been depressed during the entire week. He was preoccupied in a sad, thoughtful silence. The fiasco of the steers was a terrible blow. When the Dead Animal Removal Service from the Zulu Tallow Company hauled away most of them, his chin beneath the wide brim of his hat had trembled for a moment before he turned his head away.

He sat now at the table eating his sandwich and study-

65

ing his account book. "I don't think we're going to make it, Mary," he said at last. "I don't know whether I can collect insurance on the dead cattle or not. They'll probably be a total loss. The corn is ruined, the sows have only 3.4 pigs to the litter, and most of the cows aren't going to calve this year. We still have to buy feed for them and the steers, too. The steers aren't gaining as much as they should in this hot weather. We'll have to feed them a lot longer than I'd planned. Everything is going out, and nothing is coming in. We're pretty close to the edge of the cliff."

What could I say? I tried to comfort him with small bones of hope, but it was useless. There wasn't much to be hopeful about.

"It just takes a hell of a lot more money than I have to get started. Tomorrow I've got to be back at the office. I took this week off, and if I stay away any longer I'll probably get fired. Then nobody eats.

"What discourages me the most," he continued, "is that I was stupid enough to buy Western cattle. I might have known if the grass out there had burned up they wouldn't be in good enough shape to make such a long journey in this heat. And what the hell did I think they were going to eat when they got here? We have no grass either. We'll have to put the survivors on grain and hay and that costs money. I'm afraid to look at the heifers when they get here. Just another slaughterhouse on wheels."

"Heifers?"

"Sure. Buying steers wasn't enough. Oh no. I had to invest in a carload of heifers, too. At the price I thought I couldn't go wrong. I was going to breed them to augment our calf crop next year, or grass them through the fall and put them on grain in the winter and sell them with a good gain in the spring. I was foolish enough to think I had that choice. Now all I have to do is hire a bunch of gravediggers when

66

they arrive." Charles rubbed his tired eyes with his fists, and sighed.

"You know what Mamma always said about the darkest periods in life? She said, 'Think about something else, and they will pass. The Lord will provide.'"

"Your mother was a very attractive woman, Mary, but she never tried to farm. Also, if the Lord had to provide for all the dumb city guys who thought they could be farmers He wouldn't have time to do anything else. Let's face it. We're licked."

That night we pulled our mattress out of the house and put it on the ground where there might be a breeze. Sleeping in the house was like going to bed inside a can of lighted Sterno. We rubbed citronella all over us, and lay down.

Before we could fall asleep large black ants came out of the ground, took a whiff of the citronella, and began scampering gleefully up and down our bare arms and legs and over our faces. Then came the small fire ants, their stinging bites competing with a cloud of bloodthirsty mosquitoes whose constant buzzing was as nerve-shattering as any Chinese torture I'd read about.

We woke up at dawn, cross, tired and, of course, hot, to the sound of a stock truck rattling up the lane.

"The Western heifers," Charles groaned. "Forty-five dead heifers from Nebraska." He pulled on his pants and a shirt, and we trudged through the hot sand down the dune to the barnlot.

The heifers had stood the journey better than the steers. They were rail-thin, but they were alive. The driver had the sense to travel at night and lay over during the heat of the day. He unloaded them at barns along the way, paying the farmers for the use of their barns, hay, and water.

"I done it out of my own pocket," the driver told Charles, and as Charles repayed him from his wallet I saw what was probably our last five-dollar bill before Charles' next paycheck change hands.

We put our city clothes on over our hot, sticky bodies because there was no water for a bath, and got in the Ford swarming with long irridescent darning needles and vicious flies. Charles stopped at the pump in the lane to fill the car with gas. "It all comes out of the same kitty in the end," he said, forcing a smile, "but I have the feeling by filling the tank here I'm cheating somebody, even though it's only myself."

We drove in silence to the city. Charles got off at his office on La Salle Street. As he turned to wave his hand as he always does, I wondered if he had enough money to buy his lunch.

The house in Winnetka was like an icebox compared to the cottage at the farm. Having been closed up for a couple of weeks with the shades pulled down against the sun, the rooms were cool and dark. I kicked off my shoes and sat down to go through the mail stuffed in the brass box on the front porch. There were the usual bills which I didn't open, a couple of letters, Charles' college alumni magazine, and a mimeographed reminder of the meeting of the Lakewood Welfare League that morning. I looked at my watch. If I hurried I could make it. I put on my shoes and drove to Laura Lighter's house in a nearby suburb.

Laura Lighter, a Vassar classmate of Nancy (Gil's wife), was president of the Lakewood Welfare League. She had more money than the rest of us, enjoyed the role of club-woman, and had a part-time maid who made the canned tuna fish salad sandwiches and watery coffee she always served for lunch after the meetings.

When I reached her house the secretary was reading the minutes of the last meeting to the members seated in rows of folding chairs silently counting stitches on their knitting needles, lighting cigarettes, and communicating with one another in behind-the-hand whispers.

"Do I hear a motion to accept the minutes as read?" Laura Lighter said in her high-pitched, authoritative voice. She sat at a card table facing the women.

Somebody looked up from her knitting and made the motion.

"Do I hear a seconding of that motion?"

Somebody else seconded the motion.

"Now," Laura continued, fingering the wooden salad spoon she used for a gavel, "we will proceed with our present business according to *Roberts' Rules.*" She read something to herself from a pamphlet on the card table. "Our first consideration of the day is the shortage of bedpans in the women's ward at Forestdale Hospital. You will remember a committee was appointed to investigate this shortage, and on the committee's findings it was voted that we supply the women's ward with twenty-five new bedpans."

A murmur of remembrance stirred through the quiet room.

"Now then, the hospital reports that the new bedpans duly arrived, but that on unpacking them, eleven were found to be chipped on the edges."

"What difference does it make whether a bedpan is chipped or not?" someone in back of me interrupted.

"They always get chipped anyway," Nancy declared. "The nurses bang them down in the sterilizers."

Laura rapped the table with her spoon. "We have not reached the discussion period," she said sternly. "Before any discussion I would like to turn the meeting over to Linda Maxwell, the chairman of the committee. Linda?"

Linda Maxwell, a rosy-faced field hockey star from Bryn Mawr who was now wearing a butcher-boy maternity jacket instead of a pinny, struggled to her feet.

"What am I supposed to say?" Linda asked Laura Lighter.

"We would like your opinion as chairman of this committee on how we should proceed."

Linda tossed her head to remove the lock of blonde hair which she had trained to fall over her left eye a la Veronica Lake. "*Actually*," she drawled, "I don't know whether we should try to replace the bedpans or not. *Actually*, I'll probably be one of the first to use the new ones, and *frankly* I couldn't care less whether they are chipped or not."

An appreciative titter came from the members.

Laura rapped for order with her spoon. "Now we'll have some discussion," she declared. "Any remarks will be directed to the chair."

Nobody said anything.

Laura's face clouded with disappointment. "Well, if there is no discussion we will vote yea or nay to replace the bedpans or let them go as they are. Is there a movement on the floor?"

"My God, I hope not!" Nancy roared with laughter, "not with all our new bedpans flying around!"

The meeting dissolved in hilarity.

Laura again banged her spoon on the table. When the room was quiet, she pursed her thin lips for a moment before continuing, unperturbed. "The next piece of business is the fund-raising campaign for a new sandbox at the Teeny Weeny Nursery School. . . ."

An hour and a half later a committee had been appointed to investigate the cost at Sears, Roebuck, of a new sandbox, while a subcommittee was formed to check the price against the cost of having the carpenter at Miller's Lumberyard in Winnetka make one.

The meeting was voted adjourned, seconded, and in came the tuna fish salad sandwiches and coffee.

All of a sudden it dawned on me how silly this meeting was. I didn't give a hoot whether the bedpans in the Forestdale Hospital were chipped or not, and neither, apparently, did anyone else. I didn't care whether the Teeny Weeny Nursery had a new sandbox. Let the little monsters play in the dirt. It wouldn't hurt them. I'd welcome some good Illinois dirt to play in after the sand in Zulu.

Sure, if you were sick in a hospital you were bound to need a bedpan, but Linda would have her baby, bedpans or no, and so would everybody else. Human beings got help somehow when they needed it; animals, on the other hand, were dependent all of the time on those who took care of them.

I couldn't shake off the feeling of sadness over the loss of the Western steers; of the sows eating their pigs; of our cow herd regarding the burned pastures with anxious eyes. And above all, I couldn't bear the sight of Charles' face, taut and worried, as one thing after another went against him. Surely the crises at the farm were more worthy of correction, if we could correct them, than eleven chipped bedpans!

That night while I was broiling hamburgers in the kitchen, I told Charles about the meeting.

"I don't seem to belong here anymore. I can't get horribly interested in the projects under discussion, yet I haven't been much good on the farm, either. I'm confused. I feel like a lemming with no sea to head for."

"Nonsense!" Charles replied. "You *are* a help on the farm. About the only real help I have. I'm discouraged, too, but for God's sake don't get fainthearted now. We'll manage somehow, but it will take blood and guts to do it."

He made a pair of Tom Collinses and brought them to the kitchen. I finished mine in a couple of gulps while Charles sat on the white table swinging his long legs and sipping his drink thoughtfully. "I had a good idea for the

71

farm this afternoon," he said. "I think we should raise turkeys for a cash crop. Read this."

He handed me an agricultural bulletin entitled, *Proper Methods for Raising Turkey Poults on a One-Family Farm*.

"It sounds as if it was written especially for us," I said. "I'll read it after dinner. Incidentally, this is our last quiet meal. Jan and Maria will be home tomorrow."

CHAPTER
7

In November Maria broke her right leg and left arm playing football in the vacant lot behind Florence Harp's house. She was bedridden until she could have a walking cast.

"Maria has a lot of friends," Charles observed after we'd packed off the afternoon visitors and were picking up pieces of airplane models, jigsaw puzzles, and wads of bubble gum stuck to the rugs.

"This accident was untimely. Maria was doing so well in ballet Madame Bozzuto gave her a part in the dance recital on Thanksgiving. Now of course she can't make it. I'll have to let Madame know right away."

"Maybe this bust-up will knock some sense into Maria," Charles commented.

It was Florence Harp's brother, Herbie, who had made the unfortunate tackle, and the Harps, our neighbors, felt so bad about it they invited us over for drinks, bound to be laced with their repeated apologies.

"Do we have to go?" Charles asked. He had just received a new batch of agricultural bulletins he wanted to read.

"If we don't go the Harps will think we're mad at them; it would look as if we were holding Maria's broken bones against them. You go on ahead of me. Dr. Young is coming in to see Maria and as soon as he leaves I'll walk over."

Charles straightened his tie and combed his hair, bending his knees in front of the small framed mirror in the hall.

"This damned mirror is hung too low," he complained, as he did every time he looked at it. (If he had his way the mirror and our pictures, too, would look like postage stamps stuck at the very top of envelopes.)

"I'll fix it," I said, giving him my standard answer.

After he'd gone, I went into Maria's room with my sewing basket overflowing with holey socks and underwear needing buttons and new straps. In her boy's striped pajamas she was sitting up in bed gluing an airplane model with one hand, using her good knee for support. The leg in the cast lay across the nightspread like a Doric column. Her portable phonograph was playing "Fit as a Fiddle and Ready for Love," a rather inappropriate selection, it seemed to me.

Jan had stopped galloping her imaginary horses all over the house, and was sitting at Maria's desk writing a letter to Miss Pearl and Miss Diamond, to whom she invariably appealed for help when she was in tight quarters. This evening she was asking them if they would please see to it that she passed her math test the following day.

"Why don't you study for the test instead of depending on Miss Pearl and Miss Diamond?" I asked.

"Shhh!" she replied, holding up a silencing hand as she continued writing.

"Do you think Jan has a screw loose someplace?" Maria demanded over the noise of the phonograph.

"I don't know. There are times I believe she has. Like right now."

"I think her behavior is the result of an overactive imagination and the need to rely on forces she considers stronger than her own. We've been studying that in mental hygiene in school. Jan is a perfect case history."

"Stop picking on me," Jan retorted without looking up from her writing.

"You'll probably outgrow your eccentricities in time," her sister observed, "but I wouldn't bet on it."

74

The doorbell rang, and I went down to let Dr. Young in. He chatted with Maria a few minutes, tried to exhibit a lively interest in the autographs and grotesque pictures ornamenting her cast, drank a glass of sherry with me, and departed.

I was putting on some lipstick before joining Charles at the Harps when I heard him burst through the front door, slamming it behind him.

"Mary!" he shouted. "Come here quick! You'll never believe what I've got to tell you!"

In his small study off the front hall he was pacing back and forth like the ancient tiger at the zoo just before feeding time. "I think Horace Harp is going to buy the farm!"

"You're crazy."

"No, I'm not. Listen! Horace asked me about the farm at the PTA meeting a couple of weeks ago, and I told him a little about it. Not much. Just that we were trying to raise cattle and hogs and grow as much of our own feed as we could, and so on. He seemed very interested and asked me a lot more questions, but I never gave it a second thought.

"Then tonight he asked if I'd consider selling the farm. I didn't think he was serious, and I gave him the old routine about everything I had was for sale except my wife and kids, you know, that stuff. But he was serious! He asked me to put a price on it!"

"What kind of a price did you put on it?" I was astonished at the cold steel timbre of my voice.

"Well, what could I say? I told him he ought to go down and look the place over. If he was interested after seeing it, we could talk price, but he insisted on my giving him a round figure."

"How round?"

"Seventy-five thousand dollars."

"Charles!"

We had been standing facing each other, but suddenly my legs turned into a couple of strands of wet spaghetti. I sank down into the sofa and began mentally counting the peacocks on the chintz.

"I don't really believe anything will come of this," my husband said as if he knew darned well it would, "but you know Horace. What Horace wants, Horace gets. He told me he'd been looking around for a place in the country where he could take his family and putter around. He said he thought a farm would be a great experience for Florence and Herbie. He called it getting out into some real country. It seems he doesn't consider Winnetka real country. He grew up in Oklahoma; his parents had a ranch outside the town they lived in. He remembered vividly, he said, going out there as a boy, watching the cowboys throw the critters at branding time, heat their irons, and sear clean through the hide."

"He's just had an overdose of the Lone Ranger. What about Betty? Somehow I can't see Betty Harp on our farm, or any farm, for that matter."

"That's all part of it!" Charles exlaimed. "Betty has terrible allergies. Horace thinks the good clean air in Indiana would help her. He says the leaf mold here in Winnetka is the worst thing for her. She sneezes all night and can't sleep, he said, and I must say the poor woman looked miserable sitting there with a wadded handkerchief in her hand dabbing her eyes and nose. But you know what really fascinated him?"

"I can't imagine."

"The turkey poults."

"What turkey poults?"

"The ones I haven't put in yet. I told you about them. I gave you the bulletin to read on the proper methods of raising turkey poults on a one-family farm. Don't you remember?"

"Vaguely."

"Well, I haven't got around to putting them in, but I certainly intend to. Anyway, Horace liked the idea immensely. He said he figured he could handle an operation like that himself because it wouldn't entail any heavy work. The kids, he said, would help him. They could gather all the eggs."

"Do turkey poults lay eggs?"

Charles looked puzzled, then annoyed. "I don't know whether they do, or don't. I haven't read up on it, but I should think they would. Anyway, that's not the point. Not now. The point is, do we want to sell if it comes to a deal? What do you say?"

"I say that $75,000 is one hell of a lot of money. It would pay all our bills, take the kids through college, buy us a membership at the club so we wouldn't always have to go on Millicent's guest card, and we could all go to Europe next summer."

Charles looked slightly uncomfortable. "Leaving the money out of it," he said, "how do you feel about the farm?"

"I can't leave the money out of it."

Charles lit a cigarette and began pacing again.

"Anyway, what's the use of getting our hopes up until Horace has seen the place and decides whether or not he wants it? It's silly."

"I realize that." Charles put his cigarette out, and sank deep into his reading chair. "I told Horace to take his family to the farm over the long Thanksgiving weekend. They can stay in our house and try it out. If he likes it we can talk about selling it when he gets back. I only wanted your reactions now."

My reactions! My reactions were that if Horace Harp bought the farm we'd have more money than we'd have for years. It might be a long, long time before Charles was made a partner or the stock market produced some sort of miracle. My reactions were that it would be nothing short of celestial not to have to pack up every Friday, toting ice, other things we couldn't get in Zulu, the birdcage, hamsters, puppies, and other pets of the girls', plus the girls themselves; then do the work of a field hand before loading up again for the drive back Monday morning at six, delivering Charles to his office and the girls to school. The thought of spending all future weekends, holidays, and vacations slopping hogs and digging trenches for chinch bugs didn't appeal to me.

Yet there were other considerations. Charles loved the farm. The work and responsibility of the place added to that of his business in Chicago was a heavy load for him to carry, but it seemed to agree with him. He would miss it.

Also, in spite of all the trouble involved, I had to admit to a kind of nagging interest in the various projects we had started. I had an affection for the sad-eyed black cows even though I honestly couldn't identify them as individuals. They all looked alike. And the hogs. They were as impersonal as earthmoving machines and just as effective, rooting up the little sod we had with their aggressive snouts. Should we lump them and the other responsibilities we had taken upon ourselves without seeing them through to the end, if, indeed, there was an end to anything on a farm? Well, why not? Getting rid of all these problems would be something like finally shaking off a persistent winter cold gradually sapping energy and spirit.

"Since you've asked me," I told Charles, "I believe my reactions indicate we should sell."

"I guess you're right," he replied. "I am inclined to feel the same way. All things and everybody considered," he added wistfully.

In bed that night I couldn't keep my mind on the book I was reading. I kept reading the same paragraph over and over without absorbing its meaning. Charles, who had turned off his light, flopped like a fish from one side to the other in a restless half-sleep.

How could Horace Harp have inflicted this disturbing decision upon us? Did he really want the farm? I couldn't believe he did, but Horace was a peculiar fellow. He had invented some trick gadget for pinball machines that had made him (so our friends who knew him better than we did told us), over a million dollars. He had retired from business and was forever taking flyers in what Charles called wildcat stocks. He bought and sold businesses at the drop of a hat, grew the tallest delphinium on the block, and hooked up an ingenious arrangement between his phonograph and mahogany bar so that when the lid was lifted the bar played "How Dry I Am" and everybody laughed. In his snappy little bow ties beneath his perpetual Bugs Bunny smile he was considered kind of a nut, but smart. Would he be nutty enough to buy the farm? Or would his smartness prevail in the end to the point of backing down?

I closed my book, turned off the light, and in a vain attempt to forget the Harps, made a mental list of the errands to be done in the village, including a visit to Madame Bozzuto's dance studio to explain that Maria would not be able to take part in the Thanksgiving Day recital.

CHAPTER
8

Madame Bozzuto had been to the well of the fifth decade, but she was as strong as pig iron, almost psychopathic in her devotion to her art, and as temperamental as a filly in the spring.

I found her in a leotard, black tights and pink ballet slippers limbering up at the *barre* in her studio, performing energetic *ronde des jambes*. Her peroxided bangs across her seamy forehead were limp with sweat.

"You can't do this to me!" she cried when I explained about Maria's broken leg and arm. "She's one of the four flames! There have to be four. Three flames would upset the choreography which I wrote myself!"

"I'm terribly sorry."

"Don't you think the doctors will remove the casts sooner than they originally planned? They often do."

"I'm afraid not."

Madame threw a lavender shawl around her shoulders and, gracefully folding her legs beneath her, sank with a sigh onto a leopard-skin cushion at one side of the large mirror opposite the *barre*. She clasped her bird-of-paradise hands over her black cotton knees, and said sadly, "This should not happen to an *artiste*."

"I'm sure it shouldn't." I felt very sorry for her.

"What am I to do? All year I work for my recital with— shall we say mediocre talent?—and just when rehearsals are shaping up something like this happens."

"It must be dreadful."

Madame Bozzuto regarded me thoughtfully. "Am I mistaken, or did this rather clumsy child of yours tell me you danced?"

"I used to. Ages ago."

"Where?"

"In Washington, D. C., I danced in the *corps de ballet* of the opera company the winter of the flu epidemic. I got the assignment only because I didn't get the flu. I filled in for the dancers who were sick. I wasn't much good, I'm afraid."

The memory of the pain and the joy of those years when I imagined myself pirouetting through life "on the points" rushed back. I recalled the hours and hours and hours at the *barre*, the floor work, the choreography of the various ballets for the opera rehearsed over and over under the cold eye of the ballet master who had a voluble and insulting tongue. "You're hopping around like a chicken again!" he would shout at me.

When the routine became too demanding, and fatigue threatened to close my eyes in the middle of an arabesque, I took the bus to Baltimore and spent a few days with Aunt Itty Bit Tyler, a distant cousin of Mamma's, who lived in a shabby old house in a part of the city that had become disreputable.

Aunt Itty Bit (so called as a child by a younger sister who couldn't pronounce her name, Elizabeth) wore long black skirts and china silk blouses with jabots fastened at the throat by a cameo brooch. She nipped from a bottle of Silver Palace gin in the mornings to sharpen her mind while she handicapped the day's entries in the *Racing Form*. Every afternoon she went to the racetrack on the trolley car carrying in the beaded bag swinging on her arm sufficient capital to back her selections at the two-dollar window. For nearly seventy years she had been a permanent fixture at the

Maryland tracks, and she had no intention of changing her pattern of living just because she was getting, as she expressed it, a little over at the knees.

Aunt Itty Bit taught me quite a lot about horse racing.

"I asked you a question," Madame Bozzuto said peevishly.

"Sorry, I was daydreaming."

"I asked you under whom did you study?"

"Chernekov."

"Ah, Chernekov! He was a great master. He was my idol when he was dancing." She stared wistfully at the ceiling in remembrance of earlier and more gratifying days.

"He was OK, but I wasn't any good. He told me I'd never make a dancer. He said my legs wouldn't stand. He was right, too."

Madame Bozzuto studied my legs stuck in galoshes. "Get up!" she commanded. "And take off those idiotic things."

I unbuckled my galoshes and stood up.

"Hmm. I see what Chernekov meant. However, beggars can't be choosers."

"What on earth do you mean?"

Dropping her shawl Madame rose from the leopard-skin cushion. "I mean," she said, waggling her forefinger across my face, "that you are going to take Maria's place in the ballet. You're the same height, and we have two weeks before the recital to limber you up and rehearse you. In that way my choreography will not be disturbed. Be here in the studio at nine every morning. I will do my best."

She glided across the floor, shot up in a *grand tour jetté* and returned to the *barre*, leaving me with the feeling she'd done me an enormous favor.

In despair I got in the car and drove to the library with all of Charles' books on agriculture he said he wouldn't need any more because he was certain Horace Harp was going to buy the farm.

How in the world was I going to get out of this miserable situation with Madame? I didn't have the courage to stand up to her and tell her I wasn't going to dance in her damned recital. I couldn't. I was stiff as a poker, and two weeks' practice wouldn't do any good. Besides, I'd make a fool of myself cavorting around a stage with a lot of kids. I could hear the horrible thumps the blocks in new ballet slippers make.

I resolved to telephone her in the morning. "I'm terribly sorry, Madame . . . no, I definitely cannot. It's absolutely out of the question. . . . Good-bye." But in my heart I knew I would turn up at nine o'clock because above everything else I am a coward. At a time like this I envied Jan with Miss Pearl and Miss Diamond to lean on. I had nobody. I certainly wasn't going to tell Charles or the girls. I could see their pointed fingers and hear their jackknifed guffaws.

"You look sick," Charles observed one morning at breakfast. "You're all humped over. What's the matter?"

"I must be getting the flu."

"Do you ache?"

"In every muscle."

"You'd better call Dr. Young."

"It wouldn't do any good."

"Why not?"

"It just wouldn't."

The muscular pain suffered after the first hour with Madame Bozzuto didn't go away as she said it would. It got steadily worse. My muscles not only ached, they played nasty tricks on me. One of my legs was impulsively jumping up and down under the table in a palsied frenzy. My hand trembled, spilling sugar from the spoon on the way to my coffee cup. My nerves were shot. The day before I'd burst into tears when the clerk at the A&P told me he was all out of artichokes.

"Well, stay in the house today," Charles advised. "Keep warm. Maybe you'll be better by tonight. I hate to ask you to drive me to the station, but it's too late to call a taxi; I'll miss my train."

"I have to go out anyway," I said dully, and picked up the brown garbage bag containing the new ballet slippers that had raised more blisters on my swollen feet than I could count.

The day before Thanksgiving Charles said, "Do we have to go to Millicent's for dinner tomorrow?"

"We do." I had made my plans carefully. Going to the farm was out of the question because Charles had told Horace he and his family could spend the long weekend there to see how they liked it. Horace told Charles he knew he'd like it, but the final decision rested with Betty. If she liked it, if the air agreed with her, he was going to pay Charles $75,000 for it, lock, stock, and barrel.

When Millicent invited us to her house I accepted for everybody. At the last minute I'd say I wasn't feeling well, and after dispatching Charles and the girls, I'd call a taxi to take me to the auditorium, get the recital over with, and be back in the house before they returned.

"Maria doesn't want to go to Millicent's," Charles declared. "She's developed a sudden interest in seeing the ballet. She says now that she has her walking cast she can manage very well. She's dying to go; apparently all her friends are going to be in it."

"Too bad. We're going to Millicent's."

"Can't Millicent come out here?"

"No, she can't."

"Why not?"

"Because."

"Well, *why?*"

"Because everybody's out of turkeys. How do you think I can scrape together a Thanksgiving dinner at this late date?"

"Millicent won't care. She only eats yogurt, and I don't want a big dinner. The kids can have a hamburger after the recital."

"It's too late to change the plans." An uneasiness burned in my stomach.

"I sort of halfway promised Maria I'd take her to the ballet," Charles persisted. "Poor kid has had a long seige with her broken leg. I think we owe her a treat."

Maria limped into the room in her cast. "Did you fix it, Daddy?"

Charles shook his head. "I don't think so. It seems that we can't change turkeys in the middle of a stream. Aunt Millicent has made arrangements to have us at her house tomorrow."

"But she doesn't care at all. I just talked to her on the phone. She said she'd love to come out and see the ballet, and that she'd bring the dinner in a basket. You know how good she is with baskets."

"Fine!" Charles cried. He and Maria exchanged a conspiring glance.

"Why do you always have to mess things up? Why can't you do what's planned?" I was close to tears again.

Maria giggled. "We know all about it Mummy!" she shouted gleefully. "Florence's cousin, Franny Masters, is in the ballet, and she told Florence you were taking my part as the Orange Flame. Franny's a Tree, and Florence said she told her you were real neat, and with makeup on you probably wouldn't look so old. Franny got seats for us in the front row."

Charles grinned. "I wouldn't miss seeing you dance for anything."

"Neither would I," Maria chimed in.

"So I see. Well, let me tell you something, Maria Adams. The next time you drop out of anything, anything at all, you can take the consequences. I'm not going to stand in for you or anybody else as long as I live which probably won't be very long."

"I told you ballet stinks," Maria responded. "Heck, I would never have gone if you hadn't made me."

At eight o'clock Thanksgiving morning Madame Bozzuto telephoned to say that the auditorium at the school had cross-booked for that afternoon by mistake, and that the seniors had prior rights to it for their tableaux of Pilgrims scheduled at two, an hour before her recital. "We're going to have to use the small auditorium," she wailed. "It's entirely inadequate. We'll have to run through the ballet before the performance to make any necessary changes. Be there at one sharp."

"Can't you cut out the Flames?" I yelled into the phone, but Madame had rung off.

At eleven o'clock I fished on the shelf of the storage closet in the garage for the tin box containing the makeup I'd used in the Washington opera. I opened the box expecting the smell of greasepaint which stirs the senses and makes you think of footlights, stage dust, and velvet curtains. Instead, it smelled like the stockyards with a south wind behind it. I took the cardboard top off the cylinder marked "Brunette Rose" which I remembered had been very satisfactory. It was rancid. It had melted during the heat of many summers, and frozen during the winters. The rabbit's fur puff on top of the rouge box had disintegrated to a handful of loose hairs, and the sticks of eyeliner lay like broken crayons.

"Are you nervous, Mummy?" asked Jan, following me to my dressing table.

"I don't know. I'm not very happy. Go down to the

kitchen and bring me up a dish towel." A "paint rag" was necessary in making up for the theater. At least it used to be.

While Jan was gone I pulled on the orange tights Madame had given me that bore sickly green-white streaks from a lousy dye job, and hooked up the orange leotard with its cape of gauze streamers supposed to represent fire. I had one pink slipper on and was crossing the ribbons of the other when Jan returned with Millicent who had just arrived. I tied a hasty bow and got up to greet her.

"Darling!" Millicent screamed. "How perfectly ghastly!"

"What?"

"You, of course. You look simply dreadful. Couldn't they have done better with the costumes? And your face! Are you supposed to be a clown?"

I sat down on the stool in front of my dressing table.

"Don't weep again, Mummy. All that stuff will run down your cheeks." Jan looked worried.

"What's that frightful odor?" Millicent wrinkled her little pug nose.

"It's the makeup," Jan told her. "It smells like the rat that got stuck in the laundry drain and died. Remember Mummy?"

"Be quiet, Jan. Millicent, I'm taking the car. Can you bring Charles and the girls in yours?"

"Of course, darling. Now don't be nervous. Everything will go off well, I'm sure. We'll all clap like thunder."

Buttoning my imitation suede jacket around me like a cape so I wouldn't crush the gauze streamers, I went downstairs. Charles was in his study off the hall reading the lineup for the Penn-Cornell game, but when he heard the thumps of my wooden toes on the floor between the scatter rugs he looked over the top of his paper. "Jesus God!" I heard him say as I went out the front door.

"Fan out! Fan out." Madame Bozzuto shouted at her

troupe assembled on the small stage. "You Trees, don't huddle. Extend your line! Now you Bushes come in front of the Trees. You're the ones who are supposed to huddle. You must look like a thicket, remember? Huddle and crouch. Closer! There. Where are the Flames? Blue Flame left center of Bushes," she read from a paper in her hand. "Yellow Flame next to Blue Flame. Red Flame take right center of Bushes, and Orange Flame next to Red Flame on the outside.

"Now where are the Winds? North Wind, where's your horn? Good. Take your place opposite South Wind. Where's the Witch? What do you mean you've forgotten your magic wand? How do you expect to touch off the fire without your wand? Your father will bring it? Well, he'd better hurry. Now the Prince and the Princess. You're fine." She ran her eye over the two principals in white cotton tights wrinkling down their broom handle legs. "Everyone in place? All right. We'll run through the opening. Music, please."

The three-piece orchestra, a piano, a violin, and a full set of drums, struck up the overture which sounded like an Indian war chant. The dancers went into the routine of stomping: One, two, three, and bend, fists clenched, elbows flung wide; one, two, three, and fling, hands thrown overhead with fingers extended.

The branches of cardboard leaves on the Trees became hopelessly enmeshed, and the Bushes, balls of bottle brushes wired together and dyed green with a child's face peeping out of the middle, couldn't huddle close enough to make room on stage for the two end Flames. I stomped and bent, stomped and flung, deep in the wing in front of the door to the men's toilet.

"Hold it!" Madame Bozzuto cried, clapping her hand to her head. "We'll have to try it again."

"You got yust five minutes," the janitor announced, peering through the velvet curtains into the audience. "You got yust twice as many peepul as the Pilgrims got."

"All right. Places!" Madame had developed a hoarse croak.

When the curtains parted the audience, lethargic from too many cocktails and hearty turkey dinners, clapped dutifully. Not realizing the applause was meant for them, everybody on the stage turned around to see what could be going on behind them. Finally they commenced stomping in time to the roll of the drums that sounded as if they had been cranked up for an important execution.

At the end of the overture Trees, Flames, Bushes, Winds, and the Witches, good and bad, slid into a pile backstage to make room for the Princess entering on her toes to pick the magic berry from the enchanted bush that was going to make the Prince fall in love with her. Her solo was threatened for a few moments because the stagehand had forgotten to tie the berries on the bushes. The Princess went to the bush she'd gone to in rehearsals and, finding no berries, made a minute inspection of each bush before she realized she'd have to fake the scene.

The Bad Witch performed her act around the kindling wood (provided by the janitor) with macabre justice. The Winds blew on schedule and the Flames, lying prone on the dirty floor, rose on cue to execute a flying ring-around-the-rosy on the points. It was during this exercise I felt my slipper loosen, the one I'd forgotten to secure after Millicent's arrival at the house.

Following the bit with joined hands the Flames shot off in different directions, performing a series of ambitious leaps to make the gauze streamers on their shoulders look like tongues of fire. Returning to the woodpile they did a kind of writhing belly dance until the Prince with the Good Witch at his side extinguished the fire, hauled the Princess off the pyre, and led her into a gentle *pas de deux*. Thus extinguished, the Flames exited, one at a time, in walloping *tour jettés*, aerial turns involving a hefty thrust of both legs.

While the Red, Blue, and Yellow Flames took their respective turns, I saw Charles' face grinning like a Halloween pumpkin over the footlights. Next to him was Jan with her mouth hanging open in an adenoidal stare. Millicent was beating a tattoo on the head of Peanuts, the Peke, asleep in her lap, and on the end of the row with her cast-encased leg extending into the aisle was Maria, stolidly picking her nose.

I gathered myself for the first of the three turns and took off. Like a bullet from a gun, my slipper shot over the footlights. There was the sound of a cleaver hitting a block of wood, a gasp, and Millicent's loud voice exclaiming, "He's absolutely knocked out!"

When I got back to the house Millicent, wearing one of Charles' sleeping coats over her velvet dress, was brandishing a spoon in the kitchen. The contents of her basket were strewn over the counters and on the white table. "*Mary*," she shrieked, "You very nearly *killed* Charles! It was *so* amusing." Waving her spoon in the direction of the stove she continued, "Tell me, how does one light that thing? I'm trying to warm the turkey."

"I'll show you as soon as I've changed."

In his study off the hall Charles, lying on the sofa with a pitcher of martinis at his elbow, was listening to the rundown of the Penn-Cornell game on the radio. Jan was holding a piece of ice wrapped in toilet paper to the egg-sized lump over his left eye.

"I know it was an accident," my husband said when I poked my head in the room. "I realize I wasn't a selected target, but if you had to fire your slipper why in hell didn't you aim it at that goddamned Peke of Millicent's? In the excitement he bit my ankle. Look." He rolled up his trouser leg displaying an enormous amateurish bandage of gauze covering his entire foot and extending halfway up the calf of his leg.

"Let's just say the whole thing was a horrible mistake."

"But Mummy, you were marvelous!" Jan piped. "When you did that arabesque on one toe I felt like crying. It must have hurt terribly."

"Where's Maria?"

"She's gone over to Florence's."

"Florence's? But I thought the Harps were at the farm."

"They were," Charles interjected, "but they came back a little while ago. It seems that there was an awful sandstorm down there, and Betty had a violent attack of sneezing. She couldn't stop. They've taken her to the hospital." He refilled his glass with exquisite care and drained it in a single gulp. "Can you imagine," he said bitterly, "losing $75,000 to a sandstorm?"

I sat down on the edge of the sofa. To my surprise I wasn't unhappy about the sale of the farm being cancelled. It was a complete mess with impossible problems, but I realized at that moment that I'd miss it if we didn't have it.

"Maybe we can still make it work," I told Charles. "Let's not give up yet."

"We can't give up even if we want to. We're stuck with it until another sucker comes along. That may be a long time."

"It'll probably kill both of us, but you know I kind of enjoy the miserable peacefulness of the evenings in Zulu."

"So do I. If we *could* make it go I feel we'd have a way of life that would be more rewarding than the rat race here."

"Shall we try?"

"Let's dance," said Charles, and emptied the pitcher of martinis.

CHAPTER
9

"That fellow Hardy was right about running a bull with the cows," Charles commented. We were in the basement of our house in Winnetka painting screens which should have been put up a month before. "Buying cows with calves at side and rebred is pretty chancey. You can't be sure if the cows *are* bred back, and you have to more or less rely on the breeder to tell you which of his bulls was the sire. In a purebred herd the sire is very important."

"I remember how disappointed you were when our best Angus heifer threw a Holstein calf."

"Even that was better than nothing. Our percentage of calves is frightening. Only 25 percent. That means we have to carry 75 percent of our cows for a whole year without a dividend on the investment. The only sure thing is to run a bull with the herd. That way we can watch the cows and also be certain of the sire."

Charles had been reading with a renewed determination the government pamphlets on livestock breeding as well as the books I'd returned to the library when we thought the Harps were going to buy the farm. I'd taken them all out again.

"There's a bull sale in Iowa," he continued, "but I don't dare take any more time away from the office. Do you think you could go in my place?"

"Sure."

"Do you really think so?" He seemed doubtful.

"Why not?" You tell me what you want to buy, and I'll bid on it."

"Well, there's a train out of Chicago at 6:30 P.M. that gets to Centertown at 10:01. You could take a taxi to the hotel, get a room for the night, and meet Art and the truck at eight in the morning. It's only about an hour's drive to the farm where the sale is being held, and I've marked in the catalog the lots I'm interested in buying. All you'd have to do is look at them, decide which is the best individual, and bid on him. Don't pay more than $600, though."

"Sounds easy."

"Can you go Tuesday night?"

"What's today?"

"Monday."

"You mean tomorrow?"

Charles nodded.

I started wiping paint from my hands, arms, and face with a rag soaked in turpentine.

The train and one of Art's goose drownders arrived simultaneously in Centertown. It was as if the entire year's rainfall had saved up for that one night. There were no taxis at the station, no automobiles, not even a pickup. I stood beneath the meager shelter on the platform; the water slid off the brim of my felt hat, rolled inside my coat collar and down my back. Raindrops bounced like javelins against my legs; my shoes overflowed on the bricks.

Finally two yellow eyes glimmered through the curtain of rain. I dove for them. "Where to, lady?" asked the taxi driver.

"The hotel. I want to get a room for the night."

"You nuts or somethin'? Ain't a room to be had in this town. Democratic convention goin' on."

"I'll get one," I told him with Republican confidence.

Beneath a slowly undulating banner that said "Welcome

93

Democrats," the room clerk at the hotel desk appeared to be in the throes of St. Vitus dance. He shuffled reservation cards, grabbed at the ringing telephone, and nervously buffed his nails against his lapel, while at the same time trying to appease the conventioneers clustered around the desk yelling for rooms.

"You were right," I told the taxi driver. "No rooms there. Let's try another hotel."

We tried the three other hotels in Centertown, then the tourist homes. The driver waited in his cab while I plunged through the rain, pounding on doors and ringing bells which no one answered.

"It looks as if I'll have to spend the night in your cab," I said.

"You can't do that, lady," the driver responded primly, "it's against the rules."

"Well, where *can* I go?"

The man scratched his head thoughtfully. "I declare I'd take you to my own house, only the missus had another baby last night and things is kindly tumbled up at home." He thought for a minute. "I got one last idee, but you ain't going to like it."

"I'd like anyplace that had a bed and a nice big bath towel."

"You mean that?"

I nodded my wet head and shivered.

He drove back toward the station, turning into a dark street flanked by a facade of old brick houses which had seen better days.

He carried my suitcase up the steps of one and ushered me into a dimly lighted hall where an enormously fat woman sat under a beaded lampshade staring at an account book opened on a table in front of her. Her hennaed hair springing from gray roots curled in a yarnlike fringe around her face as pale and plump as a nun's. Except for the spangled shawl thrown over her bare shoulders, she looked like a life-sized Raggedy Ann doll. She inspected me with the omniscient eye of a sorority housemother and told me I looked like a drowned rat. After the driver explained my predicament, she said, "Come on, honey," and heaved herself out of her chair. "I wouldn't do this for nobody but Jackie Irvin. He's a good friend of mine, and brings in a lot of business."

I followed her up a gracefully curving staircase carpeted with a threadbare Oriental runner. At the top of the stairs she turned down a long corridor of closed doors. In an alcove off the corridor several girls in bonbon-colored negligees were playing cards at a brown wicker table; another was picking out a tune on an upright piano. It was as cozy as the common room at boarding school just before lights out.

At the end of the upstairs hall, the woman opened the door of a room, handing me a key. "Lock it from the inside," she said, "and in the morning, just leave real quiet-like, huh?"

I promised I would.

The room had a bow window overlooking the street and more mirrors than Versailles. There was a table with a telephone on it, a straight back chair and a double bed draped in dirty pink sateen. There was no bathroom; only a rickety washbasin with some odd-looking articles on the glass shelf above it. There were no towels.

I took off my wet clothes, shook them, and hung them over the foot of the bed, drying myself on the pillow slip which smelled like old oranges.

As I climbed into the bed I thought of Mamma and Aunt and some of the dreary places we had lived in. I recalled what they said when Connie and I complained about our surroundings: "Anyone can stand anything for a little while."

In the morning I telephoned Charles as he told me to do

in case he had any last minute instructions about the sale. I put the call through collect, speaking in a stage whisper so I wouldn't wake anyone up.

"Where in God's name *are* you?" Charles' voice came through loud and strong. "I called the hotel last night to see if you got there all right, and they told me you weren't registered. I've been terribly worried. Where did you spend the night?"

I told him.

"Speak louder. It sounds as if you said you were in a warehouse."

"That's close enough."

"Aren't you going to meet Art? It's nearly eight."

"I'm just leaving."

"Remember now, don't spend more than $600 for the bull, and try to get one for less if you can. We're awfully pinched for cash."

"I've discovered a marvelous way to make money," I told Charles, "and I don't think it would be half as hard work as farming, either. If we can't make the farm pay and you lose your job, I know exactly what I can do."

"What are you talking about?"

"Oh, nothing."

"Don't talk in riddles, Mary," Charles said, and hung up.

The farm truck was parked across the street from the hotel. Art was slumped over the wheel, his head on his arms. He had spent the night in the cab of the truck by choice. He hadn't even tried to get a room. To Art, hotels like hospitals had their own secret dangers, and he wasn't taking any chances.

"They say in them hotels a person is bounden to be robbed, and more than likely the food is pizened." Also, he inferred there were "bounden to be a lot of 'bad' women hanging around" waiting for traveling men.

I didn't realize, nor could have Charles when he sent Art out to Iowa, that Art had never been out of Muskrat County, and like Comus' woods the world was filled with lurking terrors. He was miserable.

When I sympathized with him for the sleepless night he'd spent in the cab of the truck, he replied, "Not as I could have slept anyway. I ain't never slept a night without her. Not since we been married. I keep thinkin' about her and the young-uns, wonderin' if they're all right with me lollopin' all over the country. It may be somethin' will happen to them—or to me. Reckon a person could say I was a mite homesick." He wiped his unshaven face with the back of his big hairy hand.

"Have you had breakfast?"

"I et at a cayfe down the street awhile ago. A stack of jacks, but they wasn't like hers. They're settin' heavy as cordwood on my stomick. I drunk an orange sody to burst the gas, but it didn't do no good."

"Well, the sooner we get this job done, the sooner we'll be home. Let's go."

Art straightened his large body, started the motor, and shoved in the gear. With the stock rack rattling behind us we joggled along a narrow macadam road winding through farmland richly endowed with heavy black soil which, by comparison, made our own look like the Oak Street Beach in Chicago.

The farm where the sale was to be held was identifiable by two big canvas tents set up at the bottom of a grassy slope. Turning in the lane Art parked at the end of a long row of trucks and pickups. He cut the motor.

"Don't b'lieve I'll git out," he announced.

"But I need you to help me with the bulls." I hadn't realized how much I was counting on Art.

"Can't help it. My bowels, they ain't workin' right, and I aim to set here for a spell."

I went alone to the tent where the haltered bulls were tied to feed bunks in a continuing line against the canvas walls. Livestock breeders and farmers wandered back and forth through the middle of the tent studiously matching the numbers pasted on the bull's hips with those in their catalogs which gave the extended pedigree of each lot.

I located two of the bulls Charles had marked in the catalog, numbers 26 and 27. The black bulls stood side by side, their heads lowered to the trough, cleaning up the last bit of grain with long sweeps of their black tongues. When there was no more to eat they sighed and, folding their cypress-root knees beneath them, lowered their immense bodies onto the bedding. Their black flesh spread slowly out over the straw as if they had just taken off girdles.

Charles' comment in the catalog read: "After noting the general conformation and fleshing qualities, look carefully at the head. A bull should have a breedy-looking head." Since only the hind quarters were visible from the aisle, I squeezed between the monsters, climbed up in the feed trough and crouched low to stare into the two drowsy faces.

"Hey, you!" an unpleasant voice rasped. "What are you doin' up in them bulls' bunks?" A varmint-faced man with a roquefort complexion hustled over, his hands thrust deep into the pockets of a sleazy topcoat. His eyes jumped around beneath the brim of his tan stockman's hat.

"You hadn't oughta be up there."

I backed out of the feed bunk. "How do you expect anybody to see the bulls' heads when you've got them tied with their faces to the wall?"

"You inarested in them bulls?" The man's attitude changed quickly. He smiled a crooked smile and took my arm.

"I'm trying to decide which one I want to buy."

The breeder's eyes scampered over my face, and then

turning to a gawky youth sprawled across a bale of straw in the aisle, he whistled sharply. "Parade 'em!" he commanded.

One at a time the youth led the sluggish bulls outside the tent and posed them in a patch of sunshine while the breeder extolled the virtues of the conformation and bloodlines.

Seizing the first by the tail he held it aloft.

"Ain't he long in the twist?" he cried. "Don't he carry down good in the flank? And look at the meat over his loins! Just feel the fleshing on him." Dropping the tail he took my hand and placed it on the bull's side. "You feel any ribs?"

I shook my head.

He picked up a handful of flesh and pulled it out as if he were about to snap a rubber band. "Not flabby," he commented, "just mellow."

I said I was crazy about the bulls.

"How about having dinner with me?" The breeder's eyebrows flew up and down under his hat brim.

I thought he meant that night, but it turned out he meant right then although it was only 10:30.

Together we stood at the long wooden tables where the church ladies in heavy sweaters were ladling out portions of beans from a steaming pot and cutting wedges of apple pie. We had two helpings apiece and drank black coffee until the bottoms of the paper cups disintegrated.

When the sale was called the farmers in their denim jerkies sauntered away from the lunch tables toward the tent where the auction was to be held, turning up the visors of their striped caps so they could see better. They filed slowly into the tent and settled themselves with their orange drinks and cans of wintergreen on the board planks arranged in tiers around the wire-enclosed ring piled high with loose straw. They filled their jaws with snuff and shuffled their muddy boots while the field representative of the Angus association on the platform facing the ring droned on about the merits of the breed and the bright future of the cattle business, reminding the audience that they were just plain lucky to have such a fine consignment of bulls to bid on.

He introduced the clerk of the sale seated at a table waiting to accept payment for each lot as it was sold and, finally, the auctioneer standing beside him on the platform.

Everything about the auctioneer drooped. His hat brim fell over his ears; the sallow skin under his eyes hung in pendulous pouches; his long underwear wrinkling out of his cuffs, dangled over the backs of his hands. He surveyed his audience with widening nostrils as if he had suddenly found himself in a field of frost-nipped cabbages.

"And now, folks," the field representative concluded, "I'm turning the sale over to Mr. George Duerstenburg who will cry it for you."

The auctioneer jumped as if he had been prodded from behind by an electric loading stick. Snatching up a gavel he banged noisily on the rostrum in an attempt to shake up the bidders, replete with beans and pie, whispering to one another and belching occasionally when the soda pop took effect.

He pointed to the first lot in the ring, number 27. The breeder in the sleazy topcoat was tugging at a lead shank on the bull's halter in an attempt to make him move faster while the boy who had paraded the bulls walked behind, rhythmically whacking the animal's rear end with a cane.

"What am I bid for this graaand bull?" The auctioneer bleated. "He's one of the finest individuals I've seen in all the years I've been selling cattle, folks. He's bred in the purple, too. Do I hear two hundred?"

He didn't.

"Well, do I hear one-fifty?"

Before he had time to hear anything at all he threw up his hands and shouted, "Yes! I've got it," and settled into an

100

indistinguishable chant which sounded as if he were reciting "Peter Piper picked a peck of pickled peppers" backward. Every few seconds he threw his hands up again and hollered, "Yes! I've got it!" But what he had was a total mystery to me.

When the bidding hung Mr. Duerstenburg folded his hands and leaned across the lectern. "Now, folks," he pleaded in an injured voice, "all I have is $300. You know I can't sell him for that. Won't you please stop visiting and pay attention?" He straightened up and banged his gavel. "Three, three, three," he chanted, "I've got three, but I want four!"

Mr. Duerstenburg hugged his ribs with his crossed arms. "Somebody is making an awful bad mistake letting this bull get away. There aren't too many left so close up to Old Earl Marshall. What's the matter with you folks?" He looked straight at me.

Extricating myself from the hard legs squeezing me on both sides, I rose to a more or less standing position. "Four hundred!" I yelled.

"Yes I've got it! Now five! five, five, five, do I hear five?"

I waved my catalog.

There was a tug on the belt of my coat as a farmer behind me pulled me back in place. "You're biddin' agin' yourself, lady," he said, leaning over my shoulder.

"I am?"

"You sure are."

I kept my mouth shut.

The bull was knocked down to somebody else for $600.

Every bull after that sold for more than $800. The bidders had come to life. Orange drinks slipped down rapidly; the auctioneer wiped the sweat from his face; the clerk's fingers flew as he made out the receipts of sale. Bulls were led in and out of the ring before you could say Old Earl Marshall. Throwing Charles' selections to the wind, I bid to $600 on every lot, only to be outbid. Never had I worked so hard, so unsuccessfully, to spend money.

The last bull came into the ring. He didn't look anything like the others. He was small and he was skinny, hardly bigger than the little boy leading him by an old rope shank. It was my last chance. "Six hundred dollars!" I cried, before anyone else made a bid.

"Sold!" cried Mr. Duerstenburg, pointing his gavel at me.

In the cab of the truck Art was stretched out across the seat sound asleep with his mouth open like Uncle Henry's tarpon.

I shook him.

"I finally got one."

"How much did you give for him?"

"Six hundred dollars. Here he is now ready to be loaded."

Art looked out the window of the truck at the little boy holding the bull. "That one ain't *yourn*?" There was horror in his voice.

"Of course it is."

"But he ain't nothin' but a calf! He ain't but nine, ten months old. He won't be able to breed nothin' for bettern a year!"

"I can't help it. He'll just have to grow. It's not easy to buy a bull."

Art got out of the truck and took the lead shank from the little boy's hand. He shook his head sadly. "I'm glad it ain't goin' to be me who has to tell him I give six hundred for this little peeled hide stinker."

CHAPTER
10

The results of our efforts on the farm so far were anything but gratifying. Physically we were as hefty as a couple of weight lifters in the circus, but financially we were thin as Augustus in "Streuwelpeter" on the fifth day he wouldn't drink his soup.

We bumbled along making mistakes we didn't even recognize as mistakes when we made them. A few of our schemes were working; most were not. But we kept on planning ahead anyway. A year wasn't really a measure of success or failure on a farm, we told ourselves. In fact I learned that in Muskrat County a year was hardly ever a measure of time at all.

I fell in with the thinking of Lottie and our neighbors who measured time in seasons, rarely years. When I asked Lottie to explain this she looked puzzled.

"A person don't hardly know how to answer that. Could be that if things is goin' bad in summer, say, like the droughts and such, a person knows autumn ain't far off and it's bounden to bring a change, maybe for the better. It's a heap more practical than thinkin' a whole year ahead that things ain't goin' to be so bad next summer as they has been this summer."

Her meaning, when I finally got it, made good sense. The seasons, their arrival, their message, their departure, and replacement were punctuation symbols in the long sentence of a year's time. In addition to giving hope that help was on the way soon if things were going against you, they broke the monotony of repetitious chores. A feeder must feed his stock the year around, but he changes his ration according to the season. He cuts down the amount of grain in the fall when the cattle are picking through the harvested cornfields; he augments it during the cold winter months for warmth and growth, and lightens up again with the arrival of spring, utilizing the early rye pastures for grazing while the permanent pastures are getting a head start for summer.

I learned that incidents, too, were recalled in terms of the season in which they occurred, rather than how many years ago they took place. It was always "the winter Amy Bell broke her hip when she slipped off Reverend Cloverdale's porch." Not *which* winter, or which year. Or, "I was puttin' up watermelon pickles the summer Ma Hollenstetter's canaries excaped and flew over to the Childers place." Or, "We was to the layin' out of 'Tater Bug Miller's Ma the autumn Othie Struber and Bully Boy Herburger (the sheriff) come back from that fishin' trip in Wisconsin with one of them muskies they'd took. Had it packed in ice and brung it clean home with them so folks could see for theirselves it weighed right around seventeen pounds."

A year was too long a time to reckon with for anybody but Charles, who had to think that far ahead and then some.

As the seasons came and went we found we were increasingly eager to get off from town on Friday night and more reluctant to leave the farm at six o'clock Monday morning for the drive back. In spite of the many discouragements, the problems we were unable to solve, the cramped living quarters in the small house, we were becoming enmeshed in the fortunes and life of the farm, for better or worse.

The girls took a lively interest in their own pursuits: their hospital for wounded birds; the tadpoles they caught in the creek and put in a tank, looking at them every few

104

minutes to see if they'd turned into frogs; the turtle nest on the ditch bank they hovered over waiting for baby turtles to crawl out of the eggs buried in the mound they kept digging up. They had their own problems and sorrows, too. The white rats Jan brought in a cage from Winnetka (the white rats had replaced the hamsters) met an unfortunate death when left on a fence post where they suffered a sunstroke.

At the supper table, conversation flew around like the canaries Ma Hollenstetter raised to sell for a cash crop. Everybody shared the experiences of the day, and opinions were liberally offered on the best way to proceed with Charles' various programs.

After supper we'd drive the pickup into the east pasture, park it at the edge of the woods, and cut the motor. It was fascinating to observe the cow herd getting ready for the night.

This was the time, the final hour of the day, when the mother cows grazed most earnestly. It was also the time the calves played their amusing games, games as patterned as tag, hide-and-seek, and sardines. They seemed to feel a sudden surge of energy akin to that young children feel the moment somebody tells them it's time for bed — when they immediately propel themselves into a kind of wild activity prompted by mischief.

With tails flung high and heads lowered almost to the ground the calves bucked and sunfished, galloping in circles on the edge of the woods. The early calves, larger and stronger than the late summer calves, took after the babies in a high-spirited romp, butting them with their heads and kicking out at them awkwardly while chasing them in a furious game of tag. Terrified, the young ones fled to their mothers for protection. When this happened the older calves dove into the stand of timber and hid among the trees where they remained as still as statues.

Perplexed, the babies bawled at their mothers who,

understanding the game in progress, rarely lifted their heads from their voracious grazing. Finally, a couple of the braver youngsters driven by curiosity walked cautiously into the woods hopeful, yet fearful, of finding their tormentors.

Then came an explosion of cracking branches and snapping twigs as the bigger calves charged out of the woods into the open to take up the chase again.

Watching our calves develop we were ever hopeful they would mature into deep-bodied, well-conformed adults readily salable for breeding stock, or for replacements in our own herd. They were becoming a family to us which needed our protection and care. We were growing awfully fond of them. The cow and calf operation held our interest above all the other interests contained within the life of the farm. To me, it was more productive and agreeable than feeding steers and marketing them commercially.

When the double-decker trucks rolled up the cinder lane to load the black steers and drive them into the Chicago yards I had to find something to do that would keep me away from the barnlot. I couldn't bear to see the steers, as complacent, well-upholstered, and glossy as middle-aged clubmen, being hauled away to their deaths in the gigantic, rattling tumbrels. I never mentioned my feelings to Charles, but I think he realized and shared, to a point, my sadness.

One dark winter Sunday morning Art banged on our back door with the announcement that our most fashionably bred heifer, the costliest of the lot, Butterfly Lady of Briargate, was having trouble calving. "I tried to pull the bugger out," he gasped into the breathtaking wind, "but she won't leave go of it. Could be it's turned around inside."

The cows were brought into the old red barn at night during the falling weather, and there in an old tie stall at the end of the barn was our best heifer in the agony of unproductive labor.

"Call Doc Stiles," Charles told me. "Quick!"

106

Within a half hour the vet braked his speeding red Chevy on the cinder lane and, worthy of the arrival of the Wizard of Oz, emerged from a swirling puff of dust.

Doc Stiles, at eighty, reminded me of an animated walking stick. His arms and legs seemed to move all at once as he pulled a pair of coveralls over his twiglike body. While he was snapping the buttons, he opened the trunk of the car, pawed through its assorted contents, and took out a stout chain and a half-empty bottle of whiskey. "Where is the heifer at?" he asked in a high-pitched, cranky voice.

He and Art and Charles entered the tie stall; the girls and I peered over the low end of its wooden side. The vet glanced at the wretched heifer standing stiff-legged, with her head drooping, her lustrous eyes staring in bewilderment at the predicament she was in.

Doc Stiles attached an end of the chain to the ankles above the tiny cloven feet protruding from the heifer. He paid out the chain as he moved a few steps backward. To Art and Charles he said, "Youse lean on her back. When she contracts, push down hard."

Art took his position.

"The both of youse," Doc squeaked crossly at Charles who was as white as a ghost and leaning against the far wall of the stall for support.

"Daddy's going to be sick," Jan whispered. "I can always tell."

"Quick!" commanded the doctor, and Charles moved reluctantly.

"Now!" cried Dr. Stiles, and gave a mighty tug on the chain.

"Again!" he shrilled, and Art and Charles bore down heavily on the loins of the heifer.

"Now wait for the next contraction," the ancient doctor told them, easing up on the chain.

Three more times they tried it.

"All right, once more," the doctor directed, and the three of them returned to their dreadful task.

The front legs of the calf appeared. Then the head, twisted to the side, the umbilical cord wrapped taut around the small black neck.

"There's your trouble," Doc commented as calmly as a mechanic peering under the opened hood of a car.

"I reckon the little critter is dead," Art remarked, blowing from the exertion of manipulating the heifer's back.

Jan began to cry.

Maria kept her unwavering eyes on the horrible progression of the unnatural birth taking place before us, but she said nothing.

"One more time and I believe we got it," Doc remarked almost cheerfully.

The final tug brought the calf to the floor of the stall. Doc dropped to his knees and turned it over. He put his head against the side of the calf. "It ain't dead yet," he reported. To Art he said, "Go get me a gunny sack."

With the sack he rubbed the calf vigorously, throwing to one side those membranes of the placenta expelled from the heifer.

"Now fetch me the whiskey." Still rubbing the calf with one hand he held the bottle in the other, taking the cork out with his teeth. He cradled the calf's head in his arm, pulled its tongue out and to one side, and poured some whiskey down the throat of the calf. Then he continued to massage it briskly.

"It sure is a nice little bull calf," Art observed. "Pity it's so weak-like."

I turned to speak some word of comfort to Jan, but she was tiptoeing through the straw in the center aisle, headed for the open doorway that was rolled back at the other end of the barn.

"So that's the way babies are born," Maria said to me in disgust. "Sign me."

Doc Stiles was holding the calf in a standing position. "I reckon he'll make it," he said. "Too weak to nurse his Ma yet, but he's gaining strength fast."

As he spoke the calf took a wobbly step by himself, collapsed in the straw, and a moment later attempted to regain his feet. In silence we watched him hump himself up only to fall back again and again, until finally he was able to stand up alone, swaying on his short legs. He uttered a plaintive sound, and his mother, who had been watching his every move as we had been, lowered her head to her firstborn. With long sweeps of her tongue she licked the furry body of her baby.

"Ain't that a good sight!" Art beamed. "Now if only the little bastard don't go and die on us!"

Charles had picked up the bottle of whiskey and was examining it carefully.

"You'd best have a pull of that yourself," Doc chuckled dryly. "Reckon you're kinda new at this."

Charles, offended at being caught out in his own weakness, replied gruffly, "I don't want any of it. I was thinking of the mother. It seems she's had a worse time than the calf. Maybe she'd like a shot."

"That heifer, she'll be all right, don't you worry. She'll clean in a matter of a few hours and she orta be good as new. It ain't always easy for a young heifer to calve, but them that does generally makes it. Worst thing about heifers is they don't show much milk."

Doc Stiles turned to Art. "You just keep an eye on the both of them for a spell. I got to get over to Ma Hollenstetter's. She phoned in that her old roan mare come up with the colic this morning."

We walked to the car with the vet and watched him put

the chain and the whiskey back in the trunk and wriggle out of his coveralls.

After he turned the car around in the crusty sand of the barnlot and swung it into the lane, we started up the hill to the house.

"Well," said Charles, "that's that." The color had returned to his face. "I didn't think the calf would make it, or the heifer either for that matter. Did you?"

"I don't know what I thought. I've never seen anything so awful."

The stinging wind lashed our cheeks. Over the ditch bank an ominous white cloud hung in the leaden sky.

"Snow," said Charles against the wind, "or maybe sleet. It's a good afternoon to go over the farm books inside."

"Afternoon?" I laughed. "We haven't even had breakfast."

"That's so, we haven't."

"I'm starved," Maria shouted, running up the hill ahead of us.

The house, warmed by the wood stove in the living room, was comforting after the cold dampness in the barn that stiffened my legs and shoulders. I put on a pot of coffee, promising Maria a cup, too, this morning. While I was setting the table in the kitchen I looked through the open door into the girls' room. Jan was sound asleep with all her clothes on in the lower bunk of the bed. Her small face was constricted in a knot of misery. A pencil lay on top of her army blanket, and in her hand was a piece of paper. It was a letter she had written: "Dear Miss Pearl and Miss Diamond, I have just scene a tearably sick cow with a calve in her stomack that wouldn't come out. Please make her get well and the littel calve to."

A lump rose to my throat as large as the egg I broke into the frying pan.

"Anyway," Charles remarked, putting his hand on my shoulder and squeezing it hard, "we won't have to bother with the birds and the bees or those books about where babies come from. The kids will be able to write their own."

CHAPTER
11

The first flock of turkey poults Charles ordered died within a week after their arrival.

"We'll get older poults," he said. "These were too little; they all caught cold."

He built a roost under the oak tree very close to the house, bought longer feeders and larger water units. He stacked the feed sacks under the house behind the wooden lattice screen that was supposed to hide the crooked towers of bricks on which it rested.

"Let's see," he mused, "from 1,000 poults we should be able to raise 995."

"What happened to the last five?"

"They represent the half of one percent loss you have to expect from injuries and things like that," he told me. "By the holiday market in November, the birds should average twenty pounds, live weight. Last year a twenty-pound turkey wholesaled right around $5.00. That would represent about a $5,000 gross. Figuring the cost of the poults and subtracting your feed, say about $100, you'd still come out all right."

"Your cost of feed sounds low to me."

"You're overlooking the bug factor, Mary. Turkeys consume large quantities of bugs."

I thought of the grasshoppers scaling the oats, reducing them to mere broom bristles, the orchestras of locusts that left a permanent buzz in your ears, the chirping crickets, and the indefinable species of insects which got inside your pants and down the top of your boots. "With the bugs we've got, every day should be Mardi Gras for the turkeys," I said, "but I was under the impression that they had to be fed very carefully and watched over all the time."

"Of course they do!" Charles exclaimed in exasperation. "That's why I'm putting them right outside our bedroom window. Why do you think I planned to take my vacation at this time of the year if it wasn't to watch over the poults? I believe if we can get them off to a good start in the next three weeks we won't have any trouble with them."

"How do you know they won't stray away from your bedroom window?"

"Because turkeys never roam very far; they like to stick close to home." Charles spoke with authority, but when the thousand poults were unloaded from the truck at their new home he had the wild look in his eye of a kindergarten teacher shepherding a large class across a busy street.

The young turkeys scratched in the sand, jumped at a bug or two, sipped some water, and fanned out over the dune, picking up their feet as if they had stones tied to their ankles. Some of the larger ones flew up into the dead branch of the oak tree.

"They seem happy enough, don't they?" Charles was radiant once more. "I think I'll feed them." He filled the trough and called the turkeys who obediently lined up at the feeders. But they didn't eat. They just stood there making huffing sounds.

"That's odd," Charles commented.

"Maybe they're not hungry."

"They must be hungry," he replied. "I'll try the sweet feed. It's supposed to be a kind of dessert you give them after the regular ration." Heaving another sack on his shoulder he carried it over to the trough, dribbling its contents on top of the grain already in the feeders.

The turkeys' heads bobbed up and down with the speed of sewing-machine needles.

"They're plain spoiled, if you ask me."

Charles grinned triumphantly. "As long as the birds eat, you know they're doing all right. They aren't sick or anything."

But he wasn't as confident as he sounded. All night long he kept hopping out of bed and running outside with his flashlight. Every time he flopped back in bed there was a fresh shower of brass knobs that rolled maddeningly around on the bare floor before they finally settled in a corner.

In the morning Lottie came over with Crystal to see the poults. She looked dubious. "I ain't never had no luck with them birds," she boomed.

"Why not?" Charles was alarmed. Lottie was very successful with the chickens she kept.

"They're all right till they go to bunchin' on you."

"What do you mean, 'bunching'?"

"Turkeys, they're foolish. Don't take too much to get them skairt. When they're skairt, they bunch on you. If you don't bust up the bunches real quick they smother."

"What scares them?"

"Most anything. I reckon a thunderstorm's the worst."

"What do you do about it?"

"You get a real long fishin' pole and swipe through the bunches. If you don't get 'em quick, they'll suffocate."

Charles looked uncomfortably at the cloudy sky.

"Also," Lottie continued, "I'd watch that hound dog of Enoch's. He's taken to wanderin' about of a night, and turkeys, they take a fright of dogs." Observing the worry in Charles' face she smiled. "I ain't sayin' it can't be done. Youse will most likely raise them birds without a spit of trouble. They look like healthy stock."

"They do?"

"Sure they do."

114

"Well, I'll go to town right now and pick up a pole."

"I thought you were going to vaccinate hogs this morning," I said.

"I am. I'll be back in a little while. You and the boys get things started."

With her clear gray eyes Lottie followed the car grinding through the heavy sand in the barnlot. "Ain't nuthin' he won't try, is there?" She laughed, and picked Crystal up in her arms. "You notice anything different?" she inquired, putting her face close to her little girl's. "A change like?"

"Her eyes are brighter."

"Ain't that the truth!" Lottie cried in delight. "And she ain't near as backwards as she was, neither. You know what I done? I been dosing her with worm medicine Doc Stiles left here for the cattle. I figured if I give her half what he give them heifers, it had ought to be about right. It sure has made a difference. I believe the only trouble was she had worms right along, and I never knowed it."

Crystal's poor little face seemed as blank as ever, but there was no doubt her eyes were brighter. Charles wasn't the only one who would try anything.

When Lottie returned to her house I walked up the hill to the hog barn where Art was leaning against the outside wall with his arms crossed over the bib of his overalls. One foot was folded over the other as he gazed with tranquil eyes in the direction of the ditch bank. The last of his winter traps was set in the hope of snaring one more muskrat or, even better, a mink.

Enoch sat in the sand resting his back against the barn, slowly picking ticks out of his hound dog sprawled limply across his knees.

"How's it going?" I asked.

The two men reluctantly put their respective thoughts aside.

"Ain't he comin'?" Art asked.

"We're waitin' on him," Enoch added, squeezing a blood-filled tick between his thumb and forefinger.

"He's gone to town, but he'll be right back. Let's get started."

Art gathered himself into slow motion. "Way I see it, we got to vaccinate these here shoats, castorate them, and ring their noses. I and Enoch'll shoot, cut, and ring. Reckon you kin catch them little buggers and throw 'em up in the bunk? It sure would save a heap of time."

The shoats, penned up inside the barn close to the feed bunk the cattle sometimes used, were squealing, rooting, and tumbling over one another in a melee of flying snouts and small cloven hooves.

I grabbed one, but before I could lay him in the bunk where Art and Enoch stood waiting with their needles, knives, and rings, he slipped out of my hands and scampered across the barn floor. It took the three of us in a flying wedge to corner him.

I sensed Enoch Ordway's disapproval of me for letting the pig get away. I remembered the time I was feeding the heifers in the red cattle barn while he stood in his cardboard topee, his jaws working over a lump of tobacco. His shifty eyes followed every move I made. Finally he said, "You ain't doin' that right at all. You're dumpin' the grain in mounds. You'd ought to pick up the sack, walk the length of the trough, and let the grain driddle out by itself."

"I can't hold the sack and walk at the same time," I told him. "It weighs a ton."

"It don't neither. It don't weigh but a hundred pounds. Myrt, my wife, she used to pick up a sack like it was full of chicken fluff. Could be you're too skinny."

"What happened to your wife?"

"Myrt? She got one of them hermias that turned into the pneumonia," he related without sadness. "She jest lay down

116

in bed one morning, and said, 'Enoch, you old son of a bitch,' and closed her eyes for the last time. Lot of spirit, Myrt had."

I was careful not to let any more pigs get away from me.

When Charles drove up to the barn with two bamboo poles lashed to the top of the car, we were on our fifty-eighth shoat. Those we'd finished were turned out into a patch of rye grass where they could eat, but the new rings in their noses prevented them from rooting up the precious pasture.

"Ain't it a mite early for fishin'?" Art nodded at the bamboo poles.

"I don't aim to use them for fishing," Charles replied, unconsciously picking up Art's idiom. "I aim to keep the new poults from bunching with them poles."

"Ain't nuthin' goin' to keep them bastards from bunchin' once they take a mind to it. Them turkeys, they're dumber than Enoch here." He laughed heartily at his joke.

"We'll see," Charles responded confidently.

Art pointed at me. "She's quakin' like a saplin' in a jimmycaine. You'd best spell her a bit heavin' up them shoats. We got bettern hundred left to go."

By suppertime the hogs were finished and so was Charles. He limped up the back steps into the kitchen. "I don't want anything to eat," he gasped, and threw himself down on the bed. He was asleep at once. He didn't even hear the telephone ring.

It was Millicent, who had agreed to stay with the girls in Winnetka while Charles took his vacation. She had gone to watch Jan's class at the riding school. "It was *too* ghastly," she screeched. "This low-grade-looking man made the girls jump their horses over things like the gates at the farm. Jan's horse did something wrong, went heels over head, threw Jan, and fell on her. Why do you let her do such idiotic things? She might have been killed. As it is she's in the hospital with a broken collarbone, and God knows what else. The doctor

117

said she'd have to stay in the hospital until the thingumabob was properly set. You'd better come up here at once. She might have a concussion, too."

"What's the matter?" Charles sat up, rubbing first his eyes and then his back.

"It's Jan. She fell off a horse and broke her collarbone. She's in the hospital. Hurry up and get dressed. We'll go straight to the hospital and then on home."

"*Tonight?*"

"Certainly tonight. Right away. Hurry."

"What good would it do to go to the hospital tonight? Jan's undoubtedly asleep. Besides, I can't leave my turkeys."

"Do you mean to say those damned birds mean more to you than your daughter?"

"Not at all. I'm just being practical. It's a two-hour drive to the city and another half hour out to the hospital. By the time we got there it would be close to midnight. Wait until morning when we can call the doctor and get a full report. If you feel you must go then, you can take the car and drive up. I can always use the pickup here."

"You're not going?"

"There's no point in both of us going. A collarbone isn't serious."

"I don't know what's happened to you, Charles. Your values have become mixed up ever since you took up farming. I don't understand you anymore. You used to be a good father."

"If there was something I could do, I'd go, of course."

"You would not!"

"I would too. You're being hysterical about a minor incident. Jan doesn't care whether she sees us or not; she's probably having a swell time with all the attention she's getting."

"How do you know she's getting *any* attention?"

118

"Because it's a good hospital. Dr. Young is a friend of ours, and he'll keep an eye on Jan. If any complications arise, Millicent will get in touch with us. Try to be logical."

"*Logical*? You tell me to be logical when our daughter is lying in the hospital with her collarbone broken and a concussion! All right, you stay with your stupid turkeys, your stupid hogs, your calving heifers, and all the other big-time messes you've got here. I'm going!"

Charles grabbed me as I went out the back door. "You're crazy. I won't let you drive up there tonight. It's ridiculous. Come back in the house. I'll call the hospital and get a report on Jan. If it's at all serious, I'll go with you."

I sat on the edge of the bed while Charles cranked the telephone on the wall. For once Central was at the switchboard, and not lying down on the cot in the next room. He got the resident at the hospital, said, "Uh huh, uh huh, uh huh," over and over, laughed once, and hung up.

"Just as I thought. No problems at all. Jan is fine. They've given her a sedative and she's sound asleep. The doctor said she could come home in a few days. Meanwhile she's happy and she is not in any pain."

"She must be terribly lonely."

"No, she's not. The doctor said she talked all the time to a Miss Pearl and a Miss Diamond, although he said he was never able to see them, or find out exactly who they were."

I burst into tears and buried my face in my lumpy kapok pillow. Charles went right back to sleep.

As I hung suspended in that nightmarish area between mental anguish and fitful sleep, I told myself that as parents our place was at home with our children, not with a bunch of animals and birds in Zulu, Indiana.

Millicent was a good scout, but she couldn't be expected to cope with emergencies. Besides, she'd invited Mr. Stan and Jon to spend a few days at our house to keep her

119

company. She would be amused by them, and you couldn't blame her if she forgot all about Jan. Why hadn't I thought to speak with Maria on the phone? She would have given me an accurate account of the situation in her matter-of-fact voice. I would call her first thing in the morning, before she went to school and before I left the farm.

Subconsciously I was aware of a distant rumble out-doors, and for awhile I imagined it was my oozing tears making the pillow so wet, but all at once my conscious instincts returned with a bound. I sat up. The rain was pouring in the window, soaking my side of the bed. The rumble came again, loud, authoritatively. Thunder! Jumping up I closed the window. A flash of lightning revealed Charles under the oak tree swabbing the ground with one of his poles. He was soaking wet; his pajamas were stuck to his body; his hair fell across his forehead in unexpected bangs as it does when he comes up in the water after a dive. His bare feet were thrashing about like a pair of whitings. The beam of his flashlight was trained on a heap of wet feathers under the tree.

Diving out the door I picked up the second pole and joined him sweeping through the wretched piles. As soon as we succeeded in scattering the birds, they hopped right back on top of one another building a new death tower. Frantically we swept and swabbed with Charles caterwauling like King Lear on the moors.

Dawn was breaking when the rain finally stopped. The gray sky was scarred with rosy gashes as the arc of the rising sun appeared over the east pasture. On the damp ground lay the evidence of the storm's damage: 482 dead turkeys. In silence we picked them up and threw them on the wagon box behind the tractor. Still in his pajamas Charles drove them out to the garbage dump.

The first time I cranked the phone Central wasn't awake.

120

I put on a pot of coffee, and tried again. No response. I fried a couple of eggs and dropped the bread in the electric toaster. No current. The Bowers was sulking. I put the bread under the broiler and cranked again.

A sleepy Maria spoke through a yawn. "There's no cause for alarm, Mummy. I saw Jan last night. After Aunt Millicent talked with you Mrs. Harp drove I and Florence to the hospital while Aunt Millicent was playing Mah-jongg with Mr. Stan and Jon. Anyway, Jan was fine. She didn't hurt at all."

"Oh good! I hope you were kind to her. Did you sympathize with her?"

"I was OK, but I didn't sympathize. Sympathy is poor medicine. It says so in the first chapter of basic psychology. The book says if you sympathize with people it makes them feel sorry for themselves, and self-pity is the most destructive of all the human emotions."

"Oh, damn human emotions! Jan's your sister. Why couldn't you have comforted her, at least until I could get there?"

"Comfort and sympathy are totally unrelated," Maria recited. "You can comfort someone, but you must never sympathize. I did comfort Jan, at least I tried to. I took her favorite white rat to her. She was very comforted until the nurse discovered it and took it away to the hospital lab in a wastepaper basket. Jan was afraid they'd use it for medical experiments. It was the only time she cried."

"What's burning?" Charles asked, coming through the back door into the kitchen. He was shivering. "It smells as if the house was on fire."

"The toast, of course. I always burn toast in the broiler. Drink some hot coffee and get out of those wet pajamas."

Charles poured half of his cup of coffee in the sink, refilling the cup from the bottle of bourbon he kept in the kitchen cabinet. "Gum Squintum," he said wearily. "Uncle Henry put it in almost everything. Said it was good for the guts."

"Uncle Henry had an answer for everything—almost."

"Why almost?"

"He never had an answer for this bitchy farm. He couldn't make anything work and neither can we. Look what it's doing to us!"

"What's it doing to us?"

"Well, you consider it above everything else. Even your children. As for me, it's turning me into an old hag with a dried prune face, stringy hair, and hands like an orangutan's. I never see my friends any more. I can't play bridge Friday afternoons because I have to come down here. I can't roll bandages for the hospital Monday mornings and gossip with the girls because I'm not back in time. I can't play tennis because I'm too damned tired, and I haven't been to a dance for two years. Right now I should be home with my daughter's broken collarbone and what am I doing? Swabbing turkeys all night long in a bloody thunderstorm!"

"You're temporarily tired," Charles replied placidly.

"I am not tired. I'm mad!"

"You're not mad. You're just feeling sorry for yourself."

"How could I feel sorry for myself? Self-pity is the direct result of sympathy and no one has sympathized with me."

"What has that got to do with it?"

"A hell of a lot. Good-bye. I'm going home where I belong."

Charles got up from the kitchen chair. "I'm coming too. Wait till I get some clothes on."

"What about your precious vacation?"

"I'll resume that later," he replied with dignity.

"And the turkeys?"

"I'll ask Lottie to keep an eye on the survivors. I'll split the profits with her when they go to market."

122

"Do you think Uncle Henry would approve of profit sharing?"

"You needn't say nasty things about Uncle Henry."

"I didn't say anything nasty."

"You were about to. I can always tell when you're going to be nasty. You get white things around your eyes."

"That's dust from the hog feed."

"Sometimes, not always."

"Well, all I can say is Uncle Henry must have thought a lot of you to leave you this rich man's Sahara and no dough. What do you say to *that*?"

Charles shrugged his shoulders. "He had a reason for doing it. He always had a reason for everything he did. I just haven't figured this one out yet." He went into the bathroom to shave.

"At least Uncle Henry could *pay* his bills, which is more than we can do!" I shouted.

"Let me handle the bills," he said. Charles' lathered face peered around the corner. "I know what I'm doing."

"I'll remind you of that when you carry me over the threshold of the county poorhouse."

Charles sneezed.

As her father predicted, Jan was bemused by the drama of hospital life. The doctor told us she could come home the following day if I would guarantee to keep her quiet, but Jan didn't seem very eager to leave.

"There's so much going on here, Mummy, and they give you grape juice at ten every morning, and again at night. It's delicious."

Her attention wandered from me to a little girl with a brace on one leg standing in the doorway. "Hi, Mimi!" Jan cried. "Come on in and we'll make up stories like we did yesterday."

Mimi sat down in the chair I got out of, and the two girls

commenced to chatter and giggle. Jan didn't even turn her head when I left the room.

Charles was talking to the intern in the hall. He had a peculiar flush on his face; I noticed the young doctor observing him carefully.

By the time we got home Charles complained of a headache and went into his study to lie down on the sofa while I made tea and took stock of the groceries we needed. Millicent, Mr. Stan, and Jon must have subsisted on yogurt and grapefruit, for there was no evidence of any food whatsoever except ten empty yogurt cartons and six eaten grapefruit halves Millicent had carefully put in the refrigerator.

When I returned from the A&P Charles was asleep on the sofa. His face was crimson and his forehead was hot. He was burning with fever.

I woke him up with difficulty. He made no sense at all, talking gibberish and fanning the air with one hand. Terrified, I called Dr. Young. He came at once. Between us we carried Charles upstairs and put him in bed.

"I'm afraid it's pneumonia," Dr. Young declared after examining him, adding that he was a pretty sick fellow and that if he hadn't improved by morning he thought he should go into the hospital.

CHAPTER
12

Charles was exchanged for Jan at the hospital. His condition was critical, the doctor proclaimed. If he passed the crisis he would make it, but we wouldn't know anything for several days. He was put in an oxygen tent and cared for by a procession of nurses whose grudging performance of their duties and gay conversation amongst themselves made me think they were more interested in movie dates with their boyfriends than in looking after Charles.

My daily visits were unrewarding. Charles didn't recognize me, and I couldn't believe the waxen face under what looked like a sheet of isinglass belonged to Charles. When I wasn't at the hospital, I carried trays upstairs to Jan at home and kept myself occupied with enormous amounts of unnecessary housework. The brass feet of the dining room table glittered, and Mrs. Snookey's walnut fakes shone from vigorous polishing. Millicent's overpowering Waterford chandelier, spreading like the Village Smithy's chestnut tree over most of the dining room, sparkled from a bath of suds and ammonia. Slip straps got sewn back on, sox were darned, and buttons missing for ages were found and replaced on the girls' dresses, Charles' shirts, and my skirt bands. If I stopped working for a moment the awful fear returned, and I wept and wished I'd been a better wife. If Charles recovered I'd never say another cross word to him. I wouldn't complain. I'd work my guts out on the farm.

The farm was the only thing Charles talked about in his delirium.

"He keeps talking about castration," the doctor told me. "I don't understand it."

"I do. It was the last thing he did before he got sick."

Dr. Young's eyebrows moved up a notch above his rimless glasses, but he didn't pursue the conversation.

Maria, in spite of her newly-hatched theories, was comforting. She never doubted her father would pull through. She refrained as much as possible from teasing Jan; she even offered to clean up her room and carry the garbage outside to the listing can in the pebbled laundry yard.

For the first time I realized Maria was changing from a pudgy-faced, ball-playing tomboy into a slim young girl with serious eyes and valid if rather ambitious objectives in life. She had decided to become a biological research doctor, and when Florence Harp came over the two girls spent hours talking about their parallel careers, for whatever Maria did Florence decided she'd do, too. Somehow Maria topped Florence in the order of peck. Florence's shaft of straight hair clung untidily to the serge collar of her middy blouse in contrast to Maria's, spiraling off the top of her head in a number of screen door springs, the result of a home permanent she'd given herself. Florence had already bought her "kit" and was only waiting for her mother to leave the house before she went to work. Maria had stopped biting her nails and so had Florence. Maria bought an orchid lipstick at Woolworth's. She overapplied it until her mouth looked like Al Jolson's. Florence's mouth on her colorless face was rimmed with magenta.

Maria still wore braces on her teeth which fired rubber bands indiscriminately around the room whenever she laughed or yawned, but they were soon to come off. It was the final step in the metamorphosis of ugly duckling to swan. When I thought of the arrangements we'd made to send Maria to an Eastern boarding school in the fall, I realized that

126

in spite of a certain relief her absence from the household would accord, I would miss her very much. Jan would be home, but at this stage of her life she wasn't very good company. All she wanted to be was a horse.

When at last the crisis passed and Charles was declared out of danger, he propped himself up in bed and demanded his books on farming and his agricultural bulletins. When he came home from the hospital he telephoned Art, asking him to drive to Winnetka and give him a firsthand account of what was going on at the farm.

The pickup truck parked in our driveway surprised me on my return from doing errands in the village one morning, but more surprising was Art in a dark suit that hugged his bulky body. The trousers, jacket, and sleeves were inches too short; he was all ankles and wrists. His ears, never especially prominent under his farm cap, stood out like handles on an urn beneath the lavender fedora on his head. His childlike face was suitably knotted in a mask of mourning, but in his clear, unblinking eyes there was a hint of eagerness for bad news, possibly even death, indigenous to the people of Muskrat County who reveled in laying-outs and other pleasures associated with deaths and funerals.

"He's awful bad, ain't he?" Art said almost hopefully.

"Not at all. He's doing fine. A little weak, but that will pass."

On the threshold of our bedroom Art paused to regard Charles lying in bed under the canopy of the four-poster. "I ain't never seen one of them oxygen tents," he whispered hoarsely, backing up a few steps.

"That's not an oxygen tent."

"It ain't?"

"It's a canopy. It keeps the drafts off in the winter."

"My, my," said Art. His malaise vanished as he examined the arch of the tester fitting snugly into the tops of the posts

127

crowned with pineapples. "A person sure would enjoy the likes of this on a cold night. Reckon it might help in thunderstorms, too." Taking a greasy notebook and a pencil stub from the pocket of his suit, which turned out to be Enoch Ordway's wedding attire borrowed for Art's trip to Winnetka, he made a few notes. "It jest might be I could rig up something like this for I and her," he commented.

Sitting down in the cretonne slipper chair at the side of the bed, he answered Charles' questions with a voluble recital of recent events at the farm. "Remember that big bull you had that know-it-all fellow Hardy buy for youse after she bought that bull calf in Ioway?"

Charles nodded with interest.

"Well sir, I'm tellin' you he's a caution. First thing, he's so fat he can't hardly waddle. Second thing, his feet hurt him awful bad. I got him turned out with the cows in the east pasture, but he won't foller 'em at all. He's taken to lying down under them piss oaks and bawlin'. If a cow, she happens to stray over to see what's ailin' him, he'll haul hisself up and cover her, but if the cows, they don't come to him, he jest lays there chewin' his cud. I and Milbert, we was out there countin' how many times a bull chews his cud to the minute. How many do you reckon it is?"

Charles displayed no interest in the equation. "Where have you put the little bull?"

"I put him in the old pen along with that white hog youse calls Fountainjoy. That little bull he takes one look at that white hog that's bigger than him and he steams hisself up and goes to buttin' them galvanized pipes that makes up the pen till they bend like saw grass in a ruffle. Then he steps out between them and takes off for the pasture where them cows is. I seen him reachin' for number forty-three. Looked like he needed a pair of stilts to get up on her, but that old cow she stood steady as can be, and the little bugger, he got

128

the job done." Art scratched his head in puzzlement. "You know, I believe that little bull is a lot older than I figured he was. His head ain't a whit smaller than the big bull's. Could be he got stunted somehow. Like one of them wharfs."

Charles' face clouded with disappointment.

"You know," Art gossiped on, "that Hardy fellow, he come by the other day and said he reckoned the big bull had been foundered afore he got him for us-uns. He says bein's he's so fat and good lookin' and the fact he don't care for cows none, we'd ought to show him at the fairs this summer along with them heifers we been crowdin' on grain. He says most likely that big bull would take a ribbon or two, and that would be good advertising for the farm. He figures we might get some buyers for next year's calf crop if folks gets a look at the herd sire. He says he can't figure nuthin' else to do with the big bugger nohow."

Charles sighed. "How are the turkey poults?" he asked wearily.

"Chipper as crickets! She ain't lost but two, and the rest is growin' so fast they'll go to gobblin' afore a person knows it."

After Art left Charles complained of a pain in his back. As the afternoon wore on the pain grew worse. By evening he was constricted by a muscle spasm in an agony of unendurable pain.

Dr. Young arrived with a morphine needle. "I can't see what brought this on," he told me when Charles was asleep, "unless he injured his back in some way before he got pneumonia. Can you think of anything unusual he might have done?"

I thought out loud of the unusual things he'd done like heaving shoats up in the trough all day, toting feed sacks, bumping for hours on end on the hard metal seat of the tractor, unloading mineral blocks from the truck, carrying them in a bent-over position to the feed bunks and into the storeroom in the barn.

"Anyone of those things could have done it," the doctor declared, shaking his head and mumbling something about slipped disks, calcified vertebrae, and poor posture. "This is a job for an orthopedist."

Charles was put first in a plaster cast, and later in a steel corset. He was told he'd have to wear it for a year. He was also told he must not lift, push, pull, or drag anything whatsoever. He wasn't told he couldn't go to the county fairs, so one morning we set off from the farm with Art in the truck and our show cattle jiggling behind us within the confines of the stock rack.

When we loaded the cattle they looked good enough to win every ribbon offered. They were fat and well-groomed — at least *we* thought they were. Art and I had sheared their faces and ears with electric clippers the night before so they would have an alert expression as if they were saying, "what's that?" The book on show cattle stated this was very desirable. But when we unloaded them at the fairgrounds and tied them up in the tent with cattle from other herds, they looked by comparison like a bunch of discarded retreads on a junk pile.

"They aren't fat enough," Charles remarked, his voice drifting down from his new height induced by the corset which made him stand like a West Point cadet at attention. "I can't understand it. We've fed them all the grain they would eat at considerable expense, yet they aren't finished half as well as the others here. Advertising our herd won't do us any good if we can't turn out better-looking stock."

"The bull looks OK," I commented, trying to cheer him up. "At least he's as fat as the other ones here."

"He's as fat," my husband acknowledged, "but he looks real stupid. Just look at him."

Lying in the straw chewing his cud, completely oblivious to the people passing through the tent examining the breeding stock, the bull, I had to admit, had rather a negative expression. Instead of seeming to say, "What's that?" he looked as if he was saying, "What, *that* old thing?" It was disheartening.

At the end of the tent Art was drinking a bottle of soda pop, gossiping with the Childers boys and Blue Burnett who had taken a summer job as herdsman for the Red Top Farm, a large cattle breeding operation in the county next to ours.

Blue stayed with the Childers boys when he wasn't traveling, acting as a self-appointed guardian of their affairs. The Childers boys, resembling the Forresters in *The Yearling* with their powerful physiques and ragged, ill-kempt beards, were apt to be rather flighty. Blue kept their account book when the hogs went to market after six months of rooting through piles of beer cans, broken glass, garbage, and plate scrapings the boys tossed out the front door of their derelict house in the woods down the road from our farm. He saw that the Childerses fed the chickens which occupied the bedrooms on the second floor of their house, and that they gave them fresh water from the bucket in the well. Saturday nights at the State Line Tavern he kept the boys out of as many fistfights as he could, and when at last they stumbled from the tavern, fighting the night with swinging arms, he conked them on the head, one at a time and, stacking them like cordwood in the back of the pickup, drove them home.

For his various services Blue took a commission on all business transactions, and had the assurance that he would always have a place to stay when he returned from wintering in the South with whichever carnival was booked at the final fair in the autumn.

"They say that Blue, he walks around with one of them sparkle-headed canes baah-'n like a billy goat to get folks into his booth, and that he trims 'em somethin' awful," Lottie had told me. "They say last winter the sheriff jumped him runnin' a crooked bingo game somewheres in West Virginia."

One day I went with Lottie to the Childerses' when Gump Childers telephoned to tell her he thought his brother, Orrie, was dying.

"Them boys always gets into trouble when Blue's away." she told me as we were bumping over the holes in the gravel road in the car Art had reconstructed from spare parts loaned by neighbors or bought from the secondhand store in Zulu. "I ain't never seen it fail. Orrie, though, he's the smart one. Can't figure out how come *he's* in trouble. Gump, now, he ain't much account with his drinkin' and gamblin' and them whore girls over to the State Line Tavern. And Blubber, he ain't a sight better. But take Orrie, he's got a head on his shoulders should he take a notion to use it."

The Childerses' house was set back from the road in a grove of half-dead oak trees. Two of the four uprights supporting the roof over the front porch had blown away in a windstorm, and the porch itself was very nearly twisted off the house. There were gunnysacks nailed over the paneless windows; no trace of paint remained on the frame siding. In the yard a few hogs were rooting through a pile of garbage.

I followed Lottie into a large, dark kitchen. She carried her kit of medicine and the doctor's book she used when called upon in emergencies like this one. A washtub filled with dirty dishes stood on the sink beside the hand pump. Cans of food half-eaten were lined up on shelves or tipped over on counters. In one corner of the kitchen a kerosine stove rested on two overturned pails. In the middle of the filthy room was a roughhewn table upon which was scattered a deck of playing cards so greasy they looked as if they had been French-fried.

Two cats got up from under the table, stretched their backs, and wrapped themselves around Lottie's ankles. She sent them flying across the littered floor.

In the doorway of an adjacent room stood a man with long black hair and a face bristling with whiskers. He had on a pair of baggy, faded trousers. A leather jacket hanging open revealed his hairy chest. He was crying like a baby.

"You at it agin', Blubber?" Lottie asked. To me she explained, "Blubber, he can't stand much pressure. He cries awful easy. Always has." She shoved him out of the way and walked into a room of bare board walls darkened by the gunnysacks nailed over the two windows. At the bottom of the rickety stairs leading to the second floor were three torn and stained mattresses; a fourth, rolled up and tied with binder twine, had been put in a corner. On one of the mattresses lay a human bundle with an avocado-green face. Lottie knelt down beside him.

"Where's Gump?" she demanded of Blubber who, shaking with sobs, had followed us into the room and was standing over his stricken brother.

"He's feedin' the broilers."

"Well, go git him."

Blubber called upstairs to his brother who tromped down the creaking treads with a half-empty feed sack slung over his shoulder.

"What happened to Orrie, Gump?" Lottie asked sternly.

"I jest don't know, Lottie," Gump shook his grizzled head. "We was all playin' cards after breakfast like always, and all at oncet Orrie he keened over on the table. I and Blubber carried him to his bed and he's been layin' there groanin' and passin' out-like now and agin'. Couple of times I figured he was gone for sure."

"What did he eat for breakfast?"

"Same as we et, didn't he, Blubber?"

Blubber nodded his head between sniffles.

"Hold on a minute!" Gump exclaimed. "He didn't neither. He had somethin' we-uns didn't. He et a stack of jacks. He's been pinin' for some of Blue's homemade jacks. He ain't had none since Blue took off with the carnival. I remember now, Orrie, he made himself some jacks whilest I was dealin' the first hand. He musta et seven or eight of them things, come to think of it."

Lottie got up and went into the kitchen. "Here's the trouble," she boomed, returning with a yellow box in her hand. "This here is roach powder. It was layin' right next to the box of mix. Could be Orrie figured it was sugar and sprinkled some in the batter bowl. He has an awful sweet tooth and besides he don't see so good anymore bein's he won't get hisself no glasses. Ain't it a wonder Orrie ain't dead?"

"I remember now," Gump Childers said. "Blue, he bought that there roach powder the day before he left. Told me to put it in the cracks in them cupboards on account the roaches was gittin' a mite thick. I plumb forgot all about it. Besides, us boys likes to race them roaches of an evening when Blue's away. It gets kinda lonely after the chickens has gone to roost."

Lottie opened her kit and took out a bottle. "This here's an anty-doty guaranteed to empty a man's stomach even if he ain't et in a week. Drag him out on the porch, boys, and I'll dose him good."

I stayed in the house alternately covering my ears and my retching throat with trembling hands.

In a little while Lottie returned with the Childers boys. Gump and Blubber were supporting their brother between them. They were laughing and taking on as if they'd been to a Fourth of July picnic.

As we drove away Lottie waved her plump arm out of the car window. " 'Bye, boys," she hollered, and the three

134

shaggy Childerses standing on their twisted front porch waved after her.

Blue Burnett's reputation was well-known throughout the show circuit. He was considered an excellent conditioner of cattle and a master showman, but he had a few tricks unknown to less imaginative herdsmen. Some of the ribbons and cash prizes he won weren't exactly valid, but the livestock judges were never able to figure out what he "did" to his entries. Blue's hand had always been quicker than the eye.

He was curling the hair on the hindquarters of his heifers now, using a Scotch comb and a fine brush. In tan coveralls he bent to his task, a cigarette hanging from his lips, his hands nimbly and expertly moving over the Black Angus. For the occasion he had bought a white straw hat which exaggerated the bluish birthmark on one side of his face. He was talking to Art without moving his lips, and Art was listening carefully between swigs of his pop.

Presently Art disappeared for a few moments. He returned with two bottles of beer which he carried to where we were standing behind our reclining bull.

"What are you going to do with those?" Charles inquired.

"Ssh," Art whispered, glancing over his shoulder. "I aim to git the beer down the bull afore I take him in the ring. Blue, he says there ain't nuthin' like beer to fill 'em out. Takes all the holes out of 'em, he says."

"That's preposterous!" Charles seized the bottles. "It's dishonest!"

A wave of sadness rolled over Art's face. "I was only aimin' for second money and the red ribbon. Blue, he says his bull's got the class won. He says there's three bulls good as ourn right now for second place, but if we'uns can fill up them hollers behind his shoulders, he thinks we can beat them other bulls. A person had ought to listen to Blue; he's been doin' this a long time."

When the class for aged bulls was called in the ring outside the tent, six overfed, overfat Angus bulls waddled sluggishly around the judges, who stood in the middle of the ring and marked their scorecards.

Leading the parade Blue threw the judges an ingratiating smile over his tobacco-stained teeth, catching their eyes and holding them hypnotically as he imperceptibly jiggled the chain at the end of the leather shank to keep his bull's head up and alert. He made a smart appearance; the judges were obviously impressed by his entry. They motioned to Blue to pose his bull in the center of the ring, which meant he was most likely going to win the class.

The noonday sun was broiling, and the bull acted as if he wanted to lie down. He probably would have if Blue hadn't kept prodding him in the stomach with the end of his cane.

"My God, it's hot!" Charles squirmed uncomfortably at the rail where we were watching the class. The steel ribs in his corset were searing his flesh like branding irons, he said.

Enoch Ordway, standing alongside of us, kept his eyes on Blue's bull. "Somethin's ailin' that big bastard," he hissed. "He don't look right."

The judges pulled our bull out of the parade and told Art to stand him next to the Red Top entry.

"We'll get second money, I'll betcha," Enoch said, but the judges, chins cupped in hands, were carefully scrutinizing the bulls in third and fourth place. Then they examined the fleshing quality of each bull in the class, running their hands over backs and ribs.

"Do youse see somethin' happenin' to Blue's bull?" Enoch jabbed Charles with his elbow.

We did see something happening. The large bull so perfectly conformed was shrinking before our eyes! His

136

massive shoulders appeared to be slipping down to his knees. He was deflating like a huge black balloon.

"Paraffin!" Enoch exclaimed. "Blue's shot his bull full of paraffin to fill him out and he's meltin' like a knot of beeswax!" He roared with laughter.

Momentarily stunned, the judges regained their poise and, drawing a line across their scorecards, sent Blue and his entry from the ring.

With the same fixed smile Blue Burnett led his melting bull through the throng of red-faced laughing spectators back to the tent.

All those who had witnessed the humiliating defeat of the great showman considered themselves fortunate. The incident would make lively conversation on many a winter night around their stoves.

With the Red Top bull retired from competition our bull won the class. A jubilant Art led him triumphantly from the ring.

"Ain't it a wonder Art he don't pop the shirt buttons across his chest?" Enoch observed, letting go with a dagger of tobacco juice.

Art gave the blue ribbon and envelope of prize money to Charles who held the ribbon reverently in his hand. He slit open the envelope and took out $7.50. "This," he whispered to me, "is the first real cash profit we have had on the farm!" He smiled extravagantly.

Our two heifers fared less well than the bull. When it was time to give them a final brushing before their class, we returned to the tent to find that one of them had gotten up in the feed trough and eaten three bulbs from the overhead string of lights. The other was in the process of giving birth to a calf.

"I never even knowed she was bred!" Art cried, seizing the protruding feet of the calf and giving a mighty yank.

"Ain't this a caution?" While he dried the newborn calf with a gunnysack he told Charles that the sire of the calf was "bounden to be the little peeled hide stinker from Ioway. From the looks of this here calf he's goin' to get us some good ones," he observed with pleasure.

After that the dwarfed bull was turned out with the cows, and the big, handsome, prizewinning bull was penned up on full feed and shown to prospective buyers as the herd sire.

Charles was more enthusiastic about the farm than he'd been for a long time. If the little bull *did* throw good calves we'd have no trouble finding buyers for them. The heifers we could sell for breeding stock, and the bull calves we could doubtless sell to the 4-H boys and girls for their feeding projects. Next year, he announced, he was going to fit the show cattle himself. It would require a certain amount of study, to be sure, but between us he saw no reason why we couldn't improve their condition and fleshing qualities.

"I realize it sounds ridiculous," Charles said, sitting down to supper at the kitchen table the night after the fair, "but that ribbon we won means more to me than almost anything I can think of. It means we are finally on our way to a successful livestock operation. Our herd has been recognized. Think of the advertising! Suppose we were lucky enough to show the grand champion bull or heifer at one of the shows! Wouldn't that be something?"

But it was going to be a long time before we or our neighbors in Zulu considered livestock in terms of winning ribbons. Though no one realized it, we were on the threshold of war, a war that was going to turn our farms into factories of meat production with the emphasis on quantity, not quality.

CHAPTER
13

It is doubtful Uncle Henry would have survived the advent of World War II without a seizure of some kind induced by his hatred of surprises and fanatic mistrust of all foreigners, particularly the Japanese. They were tricky and they were sneaky. This he had learned from a Japanese houseman who, after clearing the dinner table at night, hid all the dirty dishes in the oven for the cleaning woman to wash the next morning while he went to his room to pursue his studies of international law. "They're industrious as ants, those Japs," Uncle Henry maintained, "but you never know what's going on under the anthill."

Had he been alive on December 7, 1941, he most likely would have dealt with the situation by summoning his phantom army into a Teddy Roosevelt charge to annihilate the islands of Japan overnight.

Art had the same direct reaction to the bombing at Pearl Harbor. Hearing the report of it on his radio, he hurried through the dusk across the snow-covered dunes to bang on our door with the news.

"You know them Japs," he shouted at Charles, who was seated at the kitchen table working on his farm accounts, "well sir, they has been dropping bombs on some island that's Yew-Nited States property!" His eyes were flashing; his pink face was reddened by outrage and the stinging wind. "I aim to go home right now and load up my squirrel gun. I jest hope I get the chance to shoot some of them little bastards!"

Charles looked up wearily from his account book. "You must be mistaken," he sighed.

"I ain't neither mistaken! Turn on your radio. Them news fellers in talkin' as fast as if they got hot grits in their mouths."

We turned on the radio in the kitchen and listened to the incredible news.

"Come on," said Charles, "let's go."

An hour later we were halfway back to Winnetka. Charles, grimly silent, refused to answer any of the questions I hurled at him.

During the first weeks of the war things were, to quote Jackie Irvin, the Iowa taxi driver, "kindly tumbled up at home." People had grown accustomed to the war in Europe and recognized the probability of eventual United States involvement. But they were thrown off-balance by the surprise attack and shocked by the immediate declaration of war. After the first breath-holding moments, there was a confused scramble to take action, not always entirely patriotic.

Should one enlist or wait to be drafted? (In all probability the war wasn't going to last long.) Should one join the hoarders laying in supplies of items soon to become virtually extinct, such as new tires for cars, gas, coffee, shoes, sugar, meat, butter, and whiskey, or should one rely upon the allotments prescribed by the new ration books flying off the printing presses? How far could one actually drive with an A-card?

Charles' friends, Bob and Gil, the Chicago partners at Thurston, Dalton and Company, left to serve their country. Bob in the Naval Reserve was called up immediately, while Gil enlisted. There was some gossip that Gil signed up because he and Nancy weren't getting along well at home. In certain instances an enlistment, rather than being patriotic, was an alternate course to a threatening divorce.

140

O. G. left his office for one in Washington where as a dollar-a-year man he served in the capacity of a financial adviser to the government.

Millicent, in an olive drab uniform designed by Mr. Stan to which she added a bright red Sam Browne belt, organized a local U.S.O. She worked eighteen hours a day commandeering debutantes and other young women considered equally useless, for service at Headquarters. She made coffee in fifty-cup electric canteens, frequently forgetting to put water in them and burning out the elements.

Jan, now in junior high school, and her friends held bandage-rolling sessions, fashioning with their grimy hands loosely turned gobs of gauze which were probably disposed of in a handy incinerator when they reached their destination.

Maria, on her vacations from boarding school, no longer talked about her roommate's thirty-two-room mansion in New York, suggesting that her father should have provided similar grandeur for his family. Nor did she mention her roommate's farm in Virginia enclosed in a diamond-patterned fence, immaculately painted, which, she once scoffed, made our farm look like the city garbage dump. Instead, she and her roommate (whom Charles found intolerable without ever having met her) and the other girls at Miss Sibley's were stocking bomb shelters in the basement and under the gym, learning "first aid to the wounded," yearning to be WAC's, or preferably WASP's, and signing up for Japanese and German lessons in case we lost the war.

Enoch Ordway was drafted, but Art was declared 4-F after an examination revealed that in addition to a large family sufficient to warrant a deferment, he had a hernia and flatfeet.

"Here I been walkin' around with no arches and a busted gut all my life, and never knowed it," he lamented, and unloaded his squirrel gun.

141

Charles' cousin Robert left his law practice in New York to go as a dollar-a-year man to Washington as O. G. had done. Henry, Jr., on the West Coast came out of his pink stucco sanitorium to offer himself to his country, only to be rejected and returned to the sanitorium to fight the war on his table radio.

Just before Charles went to report to his draft board, Jan told him, "Daddy, I heard Mummy tell Aunt Millicent that if you enlisted and left her here to run the farm she'd shoot you before the Japs had a chance to: You'd better be careful."

Charles was rejected because of the injury to his back, scarred tissue on his lungs, and a chronic sinus condition he claimed was not a residual result of pneumonia, as the doctor thought, but a virus he'd caught directly from Betty Harp.

The draft board queried him on the farm, and when Charles estimated he could produce a hundred and fifty thousand pounds of beef and two hundred thousand pounds of pork per annum, he was given a C-card and told to get busy.

The raise he received at Thurston, Dalton and Company for handling Gil's and Bob's accounts in addition to his own was mostly absorbed by Miss Sibley's and the grain elevator at Zulu where we had to buy feed for our stepped-up inventory of livestock.

With Charles snowed under at his office in town, I went alone to the farm, often remaining there for long periods. Even with a C-card there wasn't enough gas to make many trips back and forth to Winnetka. Sometimes Jan drove down with me for a weekend, returning on a Greyhound bus in time for school, but she was occupied with her own pursuits at home, enjoying the prestige of having Miss Bessomer, the gym teacher, living under her roof during my absence.

I attempted to carry out the instructions Charles telephoned at night. I worked every day from sunup to sundown with Art and Lottie and Junior, who hardly ever went to school any more. The days passed quickly, but the evenings were lonely. I was too tired to read, and most of the time the radio wouldn't work, because The Bowers was sulking, so I sat in the dusk on the back steps instead of bothering to light the gasoline lamps.

There was a certain peacefulness in listening to the crickets and watching in the fading light the cows strung out across the pastures, leading their frolicking calves toward the shelter of the woods where they would bed down for the night. In the huge stillness the cough of a steer in the feedlot was as loud as a cannon. Occasionally Lottie's voice exploded across the dunes as she scolded one of her children followed by the wail of the punished child.

Uncle Henry must have spent lonely evenings at the farm, too. I wondered what he did. Did he read? Did he reconstruct in his mind the blueprints of the factories he'd built years before? Did he design new ones which would never be erected? Or did he sit feeling as lonely as I, just staring into the night?

Fortunately a greater than normal desire to sleep overcame me, and I stumbled into the house, half the time not bothering to undress before pitching facedown across my unmade bed. The next thing I knew it was morning again and everything looked better.

I took my turn on the tractor and slopped the large number of hogs we had on feed. If Art was busy repairing the busted machinery, which he nearly always was, I fed the steers, mixing cracked corn from the bin with oats and bran and minerals, and shoveling it from the wagon into the long bunks in the feedlot.

The blisters on my hands had hardened into calluses

from wielding the heavy scoop, and the muscles in my arms and shoulders bulged like a wrestler's. Once in awhile I washed my clothes in the kitchen sink, and I tried to bathe like the Schlagers, every Saturday night, but soap and water, talcum powder, even the Floral Bouquet Bath Pellets I bought at the variety store in Zulu couldn't eradicate the pungent aroma of manure clinging to my person even when I was stark-naked and just out of the tub.

"You know those purebred cows that didn't have calves last year?" Charles shouted through a bad connection one night. "I'm going to sell them and replace them with steers to step up our meat production."

He told me to run ads in the *Muskrat County Clarion* in Zulu, and in the newspapers in other Indiana towns as well. "Advertise them for $350 apiece, f.o.b. Get the cows in from the pasture and put them in that pen next to the steer lot so when the buyers come you can sell them right out of the pen. Also, take that goddamned white hog of Millicent's out of the bullpen and hide him somewhere. If anyone sees that much useless pork walking around, they'll report us."

The next morning I wrote the ads, sent them to the papers, and promptly forgot about them. We were busy picking corn. Art operated the ancient Rube Goldberg corn-picker. When the wagon box alongside was filled with golden ears, I hitched it to the tractor and hauled it from the fields to the corncribs. Lottie and Junior shoveled the corn into the elevator that escalated it up the slatted sides of the cribs and dumped it inside. The elevator worked off the power takeoff of the Childerses' tractor, which they loaned us since they hadn't gotten around to putting any crops in that year and therefore had none to harvest. The wide rubber belt around the flywheel was worn to the point of exhaustion. It kept jumping off the wheel and performing in the air the gyrations of a leaky balloon. We picked it up, took a reef in it, and replaced it. It would have been as easy to get hold of the crown jewels of Europe as a new rubber belt.

Our team worked well, but it was slow going because of the worn-out machinery. We were constantly interrupted by breakdowns. The gathering chain on the corn dump was forever snapping links and spewing them on the ground. Since Art was the only one who could repair it, he had to be hauled back from the fields along with the corn several times a day.

Earlier in the autumn we'd filled Uncle Henry's twin concrete silos with green corn cut from the muck soil before the frost hit it. I delivered the sheaves to Lottie and Junior. They fed them into the chopper which cut the sheaves and blew them up through the long pipe hooked over the top of the silo. The younger Schlagers inside the silo tramped the shredded ensilage as it rained down on their heads.

"Used to be we'd always have a goat or two to tromp," Art mused, "but with this here war goin' on there ain't even one old nanny to be had hereabouts. Good thing we-uns has a mess of young-uns. They come in handy jest when a person's about ready to drownd the lot of them." At the end of the day Lottie and I counted noses to be sure there were no little Schlagers buried under the ensilage in the silo.

One cold, rainy morning I awakened to find the barnlot crowded with stock trucks and shivering farmers. Three of them were huddled under an Indian blanket won in a bingo game at the county fair; the rest whacked their booted feet together, stamped the ground, and sniffled in the leaden dampness. Art in his torn black slicker was leaning against the barn talking over his arms folded across his chest.

What could be going on?

As I pulled on my boots and shoved my arms into the sleeves of Charles' heavy mackintosh, I remembered all at once the ads for the barren cows. The papers came out on

Thursdays; this was Friday. The livestock buyers hadn't lost any time. Most of the cows were scattered throughout the pastures; some of them had taken shelter under the ragged branches of the oak trees in the woods. I had forgotten all about getting them in.

"These here fellers say they've come to buy cows," Art told me when I joined him in the barnlot, "but I don't know nuthin' about that." His displeasure was evident.

"I do. I forgot we were supposed to run the cows into the pen next to the steer lot."

"Is that what he said to do?"

I nodded and explained the situation to the farmers who were quietly freezing to death in their summer jerkies. I asked if they would come back the next day when the cows would be penned and they could take their pick. They wouldn't. They'd wait right there, they said, until we got the cows up.

Art climbed in the pickup, and with the bullhorn blasting away he drove through the gate and out across the east pasture. I followed on Old Mae whose wet back felt to my seat like a waterlogged sofa pillow. She wasn't the greatest cutting horse, but she was all we had.

For two hours Art and I held a private rodeo in the pasture. The bullhorn usually brought the cows to the truck from which they were accustomed to receiving bales of hay, but this morning they galloped away, tails aloft, and hid in the woods. After a long game of hide-and-seek and a few lung-splitting gallops, Old Mae chucked the whole thing. She stood with her head down and her sides heaving, pretending she was going to colic.

Cutting thirty cows out of a large herd spread over two hundred acres of pasture isn't an easy thing to do. Finally we decided to take all the cows to the barnlot, confine them, check the numbers on the neck chains against the list

146

Charles had given me, and separate them there. Corralling the cows in one corner of the field, we walked them slowly along the fence line, but every little while one or two of them would break out of line and take off across the pasture at a dead run, creating a stampede by the others who followed suit. Then we had to begin all over again. It was exasperating.

It was noon before the cows were in the barnlot, pushing one another around in the crowded pen. The ones with calves bawled for their babies on the other side of the board fence, and the babies, running crazily about in the confusion of stock trucks parked like jackstraws, bawled back.

Surely, I thought, the men would go home now, returning after their dinners, but they didn't. They stood in the cold rain watching Art and me sort the cows and run them through a chute into the adjacent feedlot. The steers, surprised by the invasion, lifted their heads from the feed bunks to regard the invaders with distrust. Then they took off across the feedlot, bunched up in the far corner, wheeled around, and galloped back again.

"Jimminy God," Art gasped, whacking another black behind with his stockman's cane, "the way them steers is takin' on, they're bounden to lose a month's gain. He ain't goin' to like that."

More buyers arrived to join the early birds. There were now so many buyers that if you figured the equation each one would get only about a third of a cow, and they had all come "prepared" to buy six head apiece.

"Maybe we should hold an auction," I remarked to the farmers.

"Nuthin' doin'," said the biggest one. "I been standin' in the rain all morning snottin' at the nose, and I don't aim to have nobody outbid me. I come to git me six head at $350

147

apiece, and that's what I aim to do. I got here first, and I aim to pick out the six I want, load up, and git." He climbed into the pen with a small bucket of white paint, daubed a smear on the rumps of the six black cows he wanted, and called to Art, "Now you run them cows into the loading chute whilest I back up my truck."

"I figure I'm next." One of the three men came out from under the blanket. "I was second to git here."

The farmers proceeded on a first come, first served basis evolved among themselves, agreeing it was the fairest way to make their selections.

As I pocketed one pencil-written check after another, I wondered if it wouldn't be a good idea to sell a few more cows, ones Charles hadn't marked. The men seemed awfully eager to buy them; we might never have another opportunity to make money so fast. I had $10,050 in my jeans, an amount of money that made me giddy. Why shouldn't we try to double it? We'd be able to buy more steers, and the buyers who had arrived late and were grumbling that they had driven twenty, thirty, even fifty miles to buy our cows wouldn't go home empty-handed.

I whispered my idea to Art.

"He ain't goin' to like it," he replied. "Them other cows is carryin' calves."

"Maybe they are, and maybe they aren't," I replied.

Art shrugged his shoulders, and I sold thirty more cows.

When Charles telephoned that night his voice vibrated with excitement. He had been offered a partnership in Thurston, Dalton and Company, and was trying to decide whether to accept it or not. "If I only knew what the stock market was going to do!" he exclaimed. "It's stumbled to its knees under the burden of excess profits taxes and war losses, and none of the bright boys seem to have an idea when it will recover. If it gets back on its feet the firm will make a lot of money and so will the partners, but if it continues to dog along and the firm loses money, the partners will have to ante up. I couldn't afford that."

I thought of the $21,000 and smiled.

"And by the way," Charles continued, "I've decided not to sell those thirty cows after all. The last bulletin says there's going to be a shortage of breeding stock, and to hang on to what you've got. If you've put the ads in, kill them before the papers come out."

My tongue stuck in my throat.

"Hello! Are you still there?"

"I'm still here, but the cows aren't." I told him what I had done and my reasons for doing it. "Actually," I said lamely, "I thought of it as a patriotic gesture. You can buy more steers to feed our Army."

"Oh God," Charles moaned. He scolded me briefly, but ended up saying we'd probably be better off with steers anyway because there wasn't so much labor involved in taking care of them. "There's going to be a serious manpower shortage," he declared.

"It's already here," I told him, and got into bed with a bottle of Sloan's liniment and the $21,000 in checks.

As usual I couldn't go to sleep until I'd given small sermons to every throbbing muscle and aching joint to the effect they were being a damned nuisance and they'd better quit bothering me then and there. Just as I was drifting off to sleep a knee twitched, or an elbow shot out from under the covers, or my toes all piled up on top of one another in a vicious cramp.

I learned that loneliness could keep a person awake, too.

I would have given a crisp five-dollar bill for one of Jan's childhood hamsters, or Enoch Ordway's Red Bone hound, even though he was as impersonal as a headwaiter in a fancy restaurant, just to have something *alive* in the house besides me and the cockroaches thriving on the powder guaranteed to exterminate them.

Occasionally, I made reference to my loneliness when Charles telephoned, but he passed it off lightly. He felt I was plain lucky to be at the farm doing all the things he wished he was doing, and would be doing except he was the one who had to stay in the city and make enough money to pay the bills. Also he felt a moral obligation, since he wasn't going to be allowed to march off to war, to contribute food to those who had. I wasn't that patriotic, but there was no doubt in Charles' mind that my place was on the farm until he could get down himself to oversee the slow, exasperating process of manufacturing steaks, stews, and pork chops for the boys in uniform.

Lying in bed I thought of Mamma telling us when we became fretful, "Just remember, girls, that no one has only good days. We all have to take the bad *with* the good."

Mamma must have had plenty of her own kind of bad days, but she never complained, and I'm certain she handled them with tact and her enviable graciousness, raising her finely-arched brows and smiling her ingratiating, pearly smile.

But Mamma never had to run a tractor, slop hogs, spray cattle, tote feed sacks, paper a wall, putty a window, install a new elbow in the pipe under the sink, castrate pigs, or fork up hay.

She would not have put up with the heat stove belching plumes of black smoke and nearly suffocated everyone in our tiny living room, the smelly gasoline lamps, the disgusting performance of The Bowers, the deciduous brass knobs on the lumpy bed, or Kool-Aid. And she would never, never, never have put bourbon in lemon jello to give it a zing. Mamma was a lady.

When she and Aunt and I economized one winter by living over a grocery store in Atlantic City so that Connie could go to Miss Benton's school in Bryn Mawr (Aunt's idea), Mamma took in her stride the dismal weather rolling off the foggy ocean, the woman in the apartment across the hall who "entertained" a different man every week, Aunt's hideous cough caused by the dampness that rattled the lamp shades and lasted until spring, and the smell of rotting turnips drifting up from the grocery below. The knowledge that I was playing Japanese Ping-Pong on the boardwalk and fraternizing with the clods who blew air up the women's skirts in the fun house at Steeplechase Pier could not have comforted her.

After Daddy died Mamma's life was not easy, but she had a gift of accepting situations she could do nothing about. She was not given to worry. When she enrolled me in one of the Atlantic City public schools, there was some question as to which grade I should be put in since I had never gone to a school before. I had done lessons with Aunt and with Miss Palmer, a tutor we had one winter in Pasadena who mailed me arithmetic assignments on stationery from the Maryland Hotel after we'd left. When the principal asked Mamma what grade *she* thought I belonged in, Mamma shrugged her slender shoulders and replied, "I'm sure I don't know. The child reads a lot."

She left me to the mercies of the faculty who moved me about, first up, then down, then up again. It was confusing for everybody. The only thing I learned that winter was how to make Eggs Goldenrod in domestic science.

On those lonesome nights I also remembered the joys of our earlier days before we got so strapped. We would go to the theater in New York, dining first at the Plaza. Sometimes we went to the Plaza for afternoon tea, too, and Mamma would make Connie and me leave one cake so the waiter wouldn't think we hadn't been fed at home. To us it was impractical to leave anything as good as the pink-iced delicacy, and we whined about doing so, but then we would see Charlie Chaplin a few tables away having tea with a beautiful lady and we forgot the cake.

What I remembered most poignantly about the Plaza though, were the profiteroles, those magical, round, eclair-like pastries filled with ice cream and served with a chocolate sauce so heavy the ladle stuck straight up in the silver bowl.

Usually I could fall asleep after thinking about those profiteroles.

One morning I was awakened early by Charles tiptoeing into the house. He'd hitched a ride from one of the order clerks at his office who was going to a family funeral in Terre Haute.

"God, I'm glad to be here," my husband muttered, stretching out beside me on the bed. "I'm sick to death of the pressures of the city."

"Can you stay?"

"No. I've got to be back tomorrow. I came down today because I have a plan I want to talk to you about."

The plan was that I was to go to the university where Charles had enrolled me in the winter course of animal husbandry.

CHAPTER
14

The idea of going to college appealed to me. I envisioned myself, with black gown and mortar board, a tassel dangling over one eye, strolling slowly along a columned portico toward a library filled with scholars bent over long Jacobean tables. Because I'd had only Aunt, the tutor in California, one year in a public school, and one year in a girl's boarding school, I had not soured on education. This was going to be my great opportunity to *learn*.

When I asked Charles how in the world he had gotten the university to accept me with my limited credentials, he smiled and replied, "I bribed them."

The winter course included four divisions of livestock: beef cattle, swine, draft horses, and sheep. There were also courses in agronomy, agricultural economics, and veterinary medicine. All were obligatory. Take one, take all.

My classmates were farm-bred, farm-raised boys just out of high school who had come to the university to digest a year of college work in eight weeks. They were born knowing more about farms than I would learn in a lifetime of study. They didn't know *why* they knew what they knew, but they sure knew it.

We met in the corridor outside the dean's office, waiting our turn to be asked why we had come, and what we expected to get out of the course, and to receive the schedule of classes which began at eight and ended at five, six days a week.

"It's a bit unusual," the dean told me from the far side of his blockbuster desk, "to have a female in animal husbandry." He didn't add, especially one as old as I who had lived in the city all her life. "What do *you* hope to get out of this course?"

I said I hoped to learn about livestock management and agriculture so my husband and I wouldn't lose so much money on our farm every year.

Excusing me with a wintry smile, the dean picked up the next application.

I occupied the last available room on the campus, which was crowded with an overflow of special students and various groups of wartime trainees added to the regulars. The room was in an old gym converted to a dormitory to house a unit of Navy fliers taking a refresher course in astronomy and related sciences. When they weren't in classrooms, or doing something with or to the ancient planes parked all over the football field, they were in the showers directly beneath my room. It was like living over Niagara Falls. Because I was the only female in the dormitory, I was put on a separate floor from the young men in a cubicle hardly bigger than the oats bin in our barn. I was requested never, under any circumstances, to set foot on the floor below. Even in wartime the university was attempting to adhere to its standard regulations of dividing the sexes.

According to my schedule the first class of the day was veterinary medicine.

It was pitch-dark when I got up. The moon was shining through a light fall of snow powdering the crusty four-foot drifts that hadn't melted all winter. Carrying my new textbooks and notebooks, I climbed the drifts and plowed along in heavy boots past old buildings turreted like Rhine castles, fraternity houses, and the School of Domestic Science with

154

its delicious aroma of freshly-baked cinnamon buns until I came to the Vet building exuding nauseating fumes of formaldehyde. A climb of three-stories brought me to the classroom of Dr. Alden, a dedicated professor from New England who said "fam ennimals" in every sentence, and who obviously preferred his quadrupeds to the two-legged species of the human race.

"Our first consideration of fam ennimals," he began, "is, of course, disease. This morning we will touch on the diseases of the reproductive organs." He picked up from his desk one of four jars in which was floating a greenish something that looked like a knuckle in an Albright painting. "These are ovaries," he said pleasantly. He sloshed the horrid thing in its juice. "Can anyone tell me from which fam ennimal this one has been taken?"

Nobody said a word. The boys, in heavy sweaters and Levi's, shuffled their feet and scratched their chests.

"Come, come, speak up," Dr. Alden exhorted. "One of you must know *something*."

Since it was the largest specimen of the four, I figured a cow would be a safe guess. I raised my hand.

"Yes?"

"A cow."

"Correct."

"Now this one?" the professor continued, holding up the second jar with the same thing in it, only smaller.

No response.

I raised my hand.

"Yes?"

"A sow."

"Very interesting." He slitted his eyes and compressed his lips in a thin hard line.

"Now what about this one?" He held up the third jar.

"A ewe," I responded confidently. This wasn't so tough. All you needed to know was the size of his fam ennimals and descend the scale accordingly.

Impressed by my brilliance, the boys turned their heads and stared at me.

"Mmm," said Dr. Alden, reaching for the last and smallest specimen.

This stumped me. I couldn't think of anything smaller than a ewe, unless it was a rat. Would a rat be considered a fam ennimal? Why not? We had them in every barn and shed on the place.

"A rat?" I said.

The professor put the jar down with a bang. "All the specimens are ovaries of the cow," he exploded. "We will now proceed with the factors involved in their metamorphosis." He went to the blackboard, glaring once over his shoulder to silence the titter of amusement my performance evoked from my classmates.

The class following veterinary medicine was hog judging, held in a large drafty arena six blocks away from the vet building.

The professor of swine handed out scorecards, explaining the method of placing the class. The boys understood this quite well since they all had some training in high school and the 4-H club. We were to judge the first four places of a bunch of grunting hogs, with numbers chalked on their sides, which the herdsman was keeping in some kind of order with his long whip. We had to give our reasons for placing.

"I place number 3 over number 2, admitting number 2 is wider in the loin. But number 3 is smoother all the way through, carrying his flesh well along his sides. He is heavier in the hams, has a smaller, neater head, and is more compact. He has a well-defined arch to his back ..." I read over the shoulder of one of the boys writing on his scorecard clipped to a board.

I glanced at hog number 3. Then at number 2. They appeared identical. Number 1, on the other hand, was the largest hog.

"I place number 1 first," I wrote, "because his hams are absolutely enormous." I turned to take another look, but all the hogs had piled up in the tanbark and gone to sleep.

When the scorecards were handed in, the professor lectured on the effect of confinement on suckling pigs and its influence on the hemoglobin content of their blood. Then he discoursed on soybeans versus tankage in fattening spring pigs on legume pasture.

"What price can a hog raiser afford to pay for a gallon of skim milk when tankage is selling for $50.00 a ton, or $2.50 for a hundred pounds? One hundred pounds of high-grade 60 percent protein tankage is equal in feeding value to 1,000 pounds of skim milk. This amount of milk contains 116.3 gallons. Dividing the cost of 100 pounds of tankage, or $2.50 by 116.3, we have 2.15 cents, the comparative value of a gallon of skim milk. Please note that 100 pounds of skim milk contains 90 pounds of water."

I thought of Miss Palmer, our tutor, and laughed out loud. My knowledge of arithmetic didn't even include all the multiplication tables.

After hogs and another twenty-minute walk through the snow, came agronomy. The professor pulled down a map of the state on the wall. With a pointer he tapped the pink area. "How many come from this county?"

Several hands went up.

"You're fortunate. Best land in the state."

"How many from here?" He tapped the green area. More hands went up.

157

Finally he pointed to a gray spot I recognized as our county. "Nobody from here, I hope?"

I put up my hand.

The professor shook his head. "Pity," he said. "Very marginal."

For forty-five minutes he lectured on the basic plan of pasture improvement. He kept us after the bell rang to give us our assignments for the next day. Every one was different, and they were to be read aloud in class the following morning. One boy was to write on his experiences with lespedeza as a permanent pasture; another on the cultural methods of a given companion crop; another on the importance of scarification of seed. The professor looked at me and cleared his throat. "You might do a paper on the thirteen primary noxious weeds in the state," he said.

At noon I left my classmates hanging around a lunch stand on a street corner, gossiping about the morning sessions and about which prof was going to be the toughest. I walked the eleven blocks back to my room to see if there were any letters from home. There weren't. But the fliers had returned. The water was gushing furiously downstairs.

The line at the campus cafeteria extended halfway down the block. Inching along at a tortoise's pace, the last of us finally reached the counter now out of everything except chili and strawberry angel food cake. Dispatching my lunch in a couple of gulps I dogtrotted back to the arena where we had judged the hogs, and where the class was now assembling around the sheep professor.

"We're going to tag the flock," the man announced. He nodded at a square of portable fences confining fifty head of sheep whose faces bore an expression of mild annoyance.

The class was divided into two-man teams; each team was given a pair of shears as long as my crossed arms. My teammate went to the pen, grabbed one of the woolly

158

wethers under the chin, and dragged him back to where I was standing. Raising the wether off the ground he sat him down with a thud in front of me.

"I'll do the tagging," the boy said. "You jest keep him settin' on his butt."

He showed me how to hold the wriggling animal firmly between my knees with my hands cupped in a tight grip under his chin. Then he snipped and clipped until the wether appeared half his original size. The greasy wool lay on the tanbark like gobs of hair on the floor of a beauty parlor. The boy returned the sheep to the pen, and coming back, said, "It's all done, ma'm. You can straighten up now."

"I'm trying," I told the boy. My back was frozen in a jackknife position.

"How many of you still use draft horses on your farms?" Professor Cartwright inquired.

We were back in the judging arena after two classroom lectures on agricultural economics and marketing procedures dealing almost entirely with figures and percentages as untranslatable to me as Beowulf in the original.

Professor Cartwright, with a florid complexion and a nose like an old French taxi horn, was on the defensive because his division of livestock, the draft horse, was becoming as extinct as the dodo. There was small interest in his field. The boys snickered and paid little attention to this caricature of W. C. Fields.

"I asked how many of you still use draft horses on your farms?" the professor repeated crossly.

Thinking of Old Mae I wondered if she'd qualify as a draft horse, although all she ever pulled was a log when we were trying to stop the invasion of chinch bugs in the cornfields. I recalled the mucker I'd taken over the rat in vet medicine, and decided not to risk my neck again.

"Most farms today are mechanized," Mr. Cartwright admitted reluctantly, "but we are here to study draft horses, and that's exactly what we're going to do. Now then, has anyone here had *any* experience with *any* horses at all?"

With the question thus reframed, I put up my hand.

"Good. Belgians? Percherons?"

I shook my head.

"Clydesdales?"

"No."

"Well, *what* kind of horses?"

"Racehorses. I learned a lot about handicapping from an aunt in Baltimore."

Mr. Cartwright gulped. "Hardly appropriate here. The assignment today is the Percheron." He clapped his hands, and a stableboy trotted into the ring followed by a gray mare as large as an office building.

"Come here." The professor beckoned to me when the boy succeeded in stopping the mare in the middle of the arena. "Where is the gaskin?"

I pointed to the lower thigh.

"The elbow?"

I pointed to the top of the foreleg.

"The hock?"

I pointed to the joint in the hind leg.

"The croup?"

I put my hand on the mare's behind. She jumped.

"Whoa, Mother," said Mr. Cartwright, taking a quick step backward.

The poll, the stifle, the withers, the throatlatch, the chestnuts—I didn't miss one. I hadn't hung around Aunt Itty Bit's trainers in their shedrows for nothing.

"Inasmuch as you seem to know the points of the horse," Mr. Cartwright said tartly, "perhaps you would like to demonstrate the action of this mare."

Turning to the boys huddled together to keep warm, he clapped his hands for attention. "Never allow a showy trot to substitute for a long, springy, direct, active stride at the walk," he told the class. "The walk is the most important gait."

He instructed me to walk the mare to the end of the arena and trot her back.

Gingerly I took the lead shank from the stableboy. I could feel the 2,000 pounds of power behind it. Mother was feeling playful. She snorted a few times and, lifting one frying-pan foot after another, began to trot in place.

"Walk her!" the professor commanded.

"Whoa, girl," I whispered, and turned the mare around. She took off across the arena like a roping horse after a calf. The thunder of her gallop shook the building. Still hanging on to the shank I flew across the tanbark on my stomach and face. Mother didn't stop until she hit the wall at the far end of the arena.

"Trot her back!" Mr. Cartwright shouted, cupping his hands around his mouth.

I got to my feet, and turned the mare around. Giving her a long lead I started trotting myself. Mother responded. In a springy, four-beat cadence she followed me, her front feet grazing the backs of my boots with every powerful stride.

"Now you try it," the professor pointed to a red-cheeked boy shivering in the dampness.

"I ain't never fooled with horses none," the boy replied.

"Never mind. Try it."

The boy took the shank, walked the mare quietly across the arena, turned her, and trotted her back without scarring his rubber galoshes.

"You see how simple it is," Mr. Cartwright said to me. "You made too much work of it."

By the end of the first week I had learned that, "Farm

management is the science and art of operating the farm as a whole to secure the greatest continuous profit"; that live-stock judging consists of: "A study of an animal or animals, carefully measuring them against a standard commonly accepted as the *ideal* or *type* and that the *ideal* or *type* represents a standard of perfection combining those characteristics which contribute to, or go to make up an animal's value for efficiency for a particular purpose."

I could draw on the blackboard a diagrammatic view of the genitalia of the bull, an intricate design of retractor muscles, suspensory ligaments, seminal vesicles, and vas deferens, which bore a strong resemblance to an Etruscan vase filled with exotic flowers, all entwined.

I had learned that beef cattle are the least efficient users of feed of any of the farm animals, and that a good louse formula for the winter months is equal parts of sabadilla seed, ground flowers of sulfur, and powdered tobacco. I had copious notes on suitable rations for cattle, swine, sheep, and horses under different conditions, and I knew that a legume has nodules on its roots and bears its seeds in pods. I also learned that "squealers" were young pigs which usually starve to death and should be destroyed unless they can be made to nurse very soon after birth.

I had a nodding acquaintance with the corn-hog ratio, with factors causing variations in farm earnings, and I had some idea of the elements of marketing costs and procedure, as well as the causes and effects of limber neck, thrush, the thumps, Palisades worms, bull nose, and the wobbles.

I discovered that there were heretofore unknown bones and muscles in the human body, which under given conditions either ached or throbbed, or both. I also found that the sound of the gushing water from the fliers' showers under my room was a soporific equivalent to a sleeping pill after I

162

staggered back from the library every night at ten and fell into bed.

Gradually, however, the pieces of this bewildering puzzle began to take shape; gradually, too, mind and body attuned themselves to unaccustomed demands. My desire to learn became alarmingly vigorous. My notebooks bulged; the papers written at night for the next day's classes were a compelling challenge. Voraciously I read textbooks, charted graphs, designed hog houses, vaccinated pigs, and learned the jargon of judging: "I place number 6 over number 3, admitting number 3 is wider, deeper, more compact, smoother over the tail head," etc., etc. The word "better" was unallowable.

My classmates were no longer thirty farm boys; they were my best friends. We walked, talked, joked, and ate together. In the evening they either played basketball in the gym, or tuned up their musical instruments. I melted with gratitude when they invited me to play the flute in their band.

One dark morning when the thermometer stood at zero I was hurrying as usual to the first class of the day. In the middle of the snowy street I bumped into the dean wearing a mackintosh and stocking cap. He smiled at me. "How's it going?"

"Great. Couldn't be better." I replied between chattering teeth. "But what on earth is Sweeney?"

He thought for a moment, snuffling up the two little rivers running from his frosted nostrils. "I believe it's an irritation of the muscles of the shoulders caused by overworking a green horse, especially on sudden heavy pulls."

"Thanks," I said, "I know exactly what you mean."

One weekend I cut classes and went home. The train had originated in Charleston, South Carolina, and was bursting its rivets with a load of troops being moved to Chicago. There was standing room only. Flattened among ten home-sick sailors I stood for three and a half hours in the vestibule between the coaches. The snow sifted up through the coupling and turned all of us into white marble statues.

And once Charles came to the university. I smuggled him and his portable martinis, both against regulations, into my room, but after a night together in a narrow bed and a two-hour hog judging class the next morning at eight, he returned hungover and exhausted to the city. "I had no idea," he remarked, getting into the car with his C-card, "it would be anything like *this*."

At the end of the eight weeks the commencement ceremonies for the winter Ag School concluded with a banquet held in the Union for the graduates and their mothers and fathers. After the chocolate parfaits, each student was to leave his place when his name was called, and walk to the middle of the T at the end of the long table to receive his certificate.

The boys were scrubbed and immaculate in their best suits their parents had brought to them. Instead of the navy wool dress I described in detail to Charles on the phone, he brought an old navy school dress of Jan's, outgrown long ago and hung by mistake in my closet when it was returned from the cleaners. The pleated skirt hit me above the knee-caps. The large middy collar piped with gold braid flapped down my back. With my hair set by the local beauty operator in a jumble of sausage curls, I must have looked like a horrible imitation of Shirley Temple as I marched to the T where the dean and his faculty were seated behind an improbable floral horseshoe of yellow straw flowers and lavender glads. The dean rose, took my hand in both of his, and whispered in my ear, "We never thought you'd last. Congratulations."

164

Back in Winnetka some of our friends dropped in for a drink and to see how I had weathered the storm of education. They examined my scrolled certificate, passing it around without comment, until finally Nancy remarked, "I sure as hell wouldn't like to have A. H. after *my* name."

With her words ringing in my ears I returned to the farm the next day, highly magnified and thoroughly educated like the Woggle Bug of Oz, to try out my recently acquired knowledge.

Charles joined me whenever he could get away, leaving Jan in Winnetka with Miss Bessomer, the gym teacher who, in her black stockings and broadcloth tunic, had spent most of her life with a whistle in her mouth coaching hockey teams and refereeing basketball games. Her lips had become permanently formed around the whistle so that you couldn't tell unless you looked carefully whether it was in her mouth or not.

Maria mailed lists of elaborate items she'd like for graduation presents which we read only once before throwing them in the nearest wastebasket.

Thus we lived through the final months of the war, a period which marked for us the end of unity in our family life, for after graduation Maria was going on to college and Jan would be at Miss Sibley's.

CHAPTER

15

Charles had declined some time before the proffered partnership at Thurston, Dalton and Company, explaining that the responsibility of becoming a partner would keep him in the office all the time. He would have to give up the farm. He worked out a plan whereby he was paid only for the business he brought in. These commissions and the money he made trading stocks for his own account were fairly profitable. The important thing was that he could now spend more time on the farm.

During the war years when we were obliged to deliver our quota of beef and pork and to raise the necessary crops for our livestock feeding program, we learned where our operation had been faulty in the past. There was little margin for error; any mistakes were doubly costly because of our increased inventory. We made mistakes, of course, and paid dearly for them, but with the passing of time the place was responding to our greater knowledge of its requirements for production on a full-capacity level. The soil showed the results of correct fertilizing in abundant measure by sending up corn that was knee high *before* the Fourth of July, large heavy oats, and acre upon acre of soybeans, most of which we traded at the elevator in Zulu for corn to supplement our own output.

Charles interpreted the information I'd gleaned at the university and utilized it to greater advantage than I thought possible when I was asking questions and scribbling notes in various classrooms. Whenever we got stuck on a problem we cranked up the telephone and called a professor who usually put us on the right track.

Pastures benefiting from manure crops plowed under for nourishment yielded a decent stand of bluegrass, fescue, and a drought grass that got us through the hot, dry summer months.

The cows grazed contentedly on the improved forage, and with Professor Alden's recommended doses of vitamins, hormones, and minerals, produced calves regularly with few exceptions.

The steers were turned out in the cornfields after the harvest to pick through the stalks and to utilize the corn missed by the picker before being put in the dry lot to winter for the most part on our own silage and hay, which curtailed our grain bills at the elevator.

Even the sows showed a marked improvement; with proper minerals added to their ration they behaved like sows instead of cannibals.

We were able to pay down our loan at the bank and to replace some of the worn-out machinery so that we were no longer held up by constant mechanical breakdowns while working against time and weather.

Enoch Ordway, as dour as ever, had returned from the war to his room on the Schlager's third floor. He and Art, bolstered by the substantial raise Charles had given them, worked with renewed interest.

REA arrived like a bountiful Santa Claus, leaving us with electric lights and a refrigerator that practically threw ice cubes in your face every time the door was opened. For the first week after it arrived we had a drink every time we walked past it.

But above all good things, the farm had shown a profit for two consecutive years! After the long stormy years our ship had come in, not exactly loaded, but still afloat. We were jubilant.

One weekend, we stayed in Winnetka to catch up on things we'd neglected there. The garden was a mess of weeds, the roof had sprung a leak, and there were, as always, towers of screens and storm windows stacked in the basement waiting to be painted and repaired.

It was during this weekend I received a telegram from a law firm in Baltimore informing me that Aunt Itty Bit had passed away. I felt as I did when I was a child and woke up one morning to find my canary dead in her cage.

On the train going East I thought about Aunt Itty Bit a lot, remembering the pleasant times I'd had visiting her during the years I was trying to become a dancer in Washington. She made no demands on me or anyone, living her own life with her racetrack friends and the horses she loved to watch run in the afternoons. Her soft round face, beneath wisps of white hair escaping her net, looked as if it held a plum in either cheek. The lines around her eyes and mouth turned upward in tiny crevices of gaiety as though she had laughed at life for years and years. Short and plump, she walked like a rock dove, nodding with every step as she moved through the high-ceilinged rooms of her dilapidated house furnished with Victorian chairs with soiled antimacassers, walnut whatnots, and threadbare rugs she called druggets.

At the racetrack she not only knew every horse, his past performances and his breeding, but also the trainers and jockeys. Between the races they often strolled over to visit Aunt Itty Bit seated in the same chair she occupied every day, near the saddling paddock and the walking ring. When the jockeys were mounted and on their way to the post they lifted a finger, raised a chin, or threw her a wink in silent greeting. Aunt Itty Bit would respond, offering in her crackled voice a few words of advice: "Rate him down the backstretch, Benny, or you won't have anything under you at the sixteenth pole," or "Keep him off the rail today, dear; its gummier than a Louisiana stew."

Everyone knew and respected the old lady.

The lawyer met me when I got off the Capitol Limited, and took me directly to his office where he read Aunt Itty Bit's will. It was simple and direct. She had named me her executrix. She wished to be buried in her family's lot in the cemetery as far away as possible from her brother Bert, who had scolded her all her life for betting on the horses. Instead of flowers she wished to hold in her hand a shoe from the Preakness winner of the current year. Her furniture and bric-a-brac were to be sold with the proceeds going to her church. (If she had a good Saturday at the races Aunt Itty Bit always placed a live ticket in the collection plate on Sunday, upsetting the vestrymen until they figured out how to cash it.) Her house reverted to the mortgage company for the debt against it. The miniscule income she received from Bert's estate was to go, at her death, to his college where, as a member of the debating team, he'd enjoyed certain triumphs never repeated after his graduation. The $3,000 in cash representing her "earnings" at the track she left to me, along with her ancient Kolinsky fur coat turned by age to a startling orange-purple.

No racetrack personality, however important, could have had a finer representation of the fraternity than that attending Aunt Itty Bit's funeral held at 11:00 A.M., after the morning works and before the daily double windows closed. The only missing element was a horse, but in her small waxen hand she held the shoe of the Preakness winner, a talisman of the sport she loved so well.

Before returning to Chicago I went to the racetrack to say good-bye to Aunt Itty Bit's friends, and to make a couple of two-dollar bets I thought she'd approve.

169

A paddock sale of horses-in-training was in progress. I leaned on the rail with the horsemen watching the stock being led in and auctioned off. All at once my eye caught a two-year-old who attracted me instantly. I can't explain how or why; he just did. Maybe Aunt Itty Bit was waving the green flag at me from her new celestial home. Anyway, I knew I had to have him, and I felt that nothing would please Aunt Itty Bit more than to have her money spent on a racehorse.

Nobody urged me to buy him. The touts didn't mutter behind knuckly red fingers that I'd be making an awful mistake if I let him get away; the auctioneer didn't extol the virtues of his breeding; and the horsemen, those pantologists with the gin-clear eyes focused now upon the colt in the ring, didn't nod sagely and tell me he looked as sound as a bell of brass to them. Nobody sold me the horse. I bought him. The auctioneer knocked him down to me before I had lowered my chin. The horse was shipped to Chicago and put in the care of a competent trainer.

The sales catalog stated that he had started once that year at two. The racing chart showed that he had finished twenty-third in a field of twenty-four.

"I didn't think race tracks were wide enough to start twenty-four horses all at once," Charles remarked when he recovered from the shock of my investing Aunt Itty Bit's money in a racehorse instead of blue chip stocks. "Still, if the others were all as narrow as he is, I guess it would be possible."

To the astonishment of the examining veterinarians, the colt, whose name was Wilson Pusey, recovered from the innumerable and unrelated ailments plaguing his wretched brown body. He even got over the cough which threatened to blow his head off the end of his long, ropy neck.

After a while he was galloped on the track in the

mornings; once he breezed six furlongs in 1:21. Watching him, his trainer shook his head. "Never saw a horse move like that one; his legs all go in different directions at the same time. It's a wonder he don't trip himself."

His second race was better than his first. He was sixth in a pack of seven, but still it was a better race.

He started half a dozen times after that, and then his trainer said we ought to put him up for the rest of the season. "We'll let him grow," he said. He intimated he was running out of jockeys. "The colt has a dead mouth. The boys can't rate him at all. They just have to sit there and let him run the way he wants to. They don't like that; it's an uncomforatble feeling."

Back in his stall in the shedrow I had many visits with Wilson Pusey. I never tried to touch him, for the boy who ponied him told me, "Missus, if you go to patting that one, you'll bring your arm back without a hand."

Soon I gave up inquiring about the boys missing from the stable gang. The answer was always the same: "George, 'e got 'is this morning. Knocked the feed tub right out of 'is 'and, 'e did, and sunk 'is bloody teeth clean up to the gooms in old George's arm." Or, "Sam, he liked to get hisself killed. That old colt, he let him have it with bof' hind feet whilest he were amuckin' out de stall." The blacksmith had had it; the dentist had had it; and the vets on their routine checkups peered briefly over the stall guard and said, "He looks fit enough; let's see the next one." And they moved on up the row.

Even the dogs and the cats, the chickens and the goat that hung around the barn taking their ease in the stalls of the other horses, circled way out from under the shedrow when they passed his. It seemed as if Wilson Pusey didn't want to be friends with anyone.

I stood at his door watching him for a long time. Mostly

he turned his back to me, hanging his head in a dark corner. Thinking, I guess. But sometimes he would turn around, and pinning his ears, rush at me, his lips rolled up above his small white teeth. Occasionally he'd stand still and just stare at me. It was then that I could see the torment in his face, the tense, pinched look as if something was hurting him. I thought about it for a long time.

When Charles told me one day he had to go to Louisville on business I asked if I might go with him. I knew that Wilson Pusey's sire and his dam lived nearby. Surely one or the other might be able to give me a clue to the colt's behavior!

His business completed, Charles offered to drive me out to the country, in spite of the fact that he had one of his sinus headaches coming on. (He'd had a steady procession of them ever since he had pneumonia.) He cursed himself for leaving his new pills at home; they helped him a lot, he said.

We found the sire of the colt down on his knees in one corner of his paddock. He had thrust his head under the lowest board of the enclosure and was nibbling a fringe of green grass inaccessible to him except for his extraordinary posture. He was an agreeable horse and obviously smart. We patted him and fed him a package of square gum drops. "He likes them licorish ones best," his groom said, so we saved the black one till last.

The mare lived on a twenty-five hundred-acre farm so elaborately beautiful that it made us feel like whispering. We tiptoed across the macadam courtyard, surrounded by a clipped yew hedge, to the vine-covered stable where twin white cupolas glistened like spun sugar ornaments at either end of the long, slate roof. Every knob, latch, and hinge sparkled like gold.

"How do you suppose any animal raised on this place can be so god-awful ornery?" Charles asked.

172

The tack room to which we were directed was as imposing as a financier's library. We sank into a soft leather sofa and waited to be presented. Finally a groom nodded to us. We stepped out upon a flagstone terrace where an old Negro, shank in hand, stood at the head of a large deep-bellied brood mare.

At once I noticed the same pained, tight look about her face that her son had. If she'd been a woman she would have had a deep frown running down her forehead. Her eyes were red-rimmed, and she fastened them threateningly upon us, at the same time swelling her fluted nostrils. The Negro tightened his hold on the shank, but the mare reared, and commenced to box the air just above our heads. When the groom, dangling as he had been on the other end of the lead-shank, regained his footing, I asked him how her disposition was, sidestepping a sudden thrust from a hind leg. "Generally speaking," I added over the knot of terror in my throat.

He shook his old, graying head slowly. "She's kinda hateful, Miss," he replied softly.

At this moment a gentleman stepped out of the tack room onto the terrace. He spoke cordially and explained that he was Rufus Tate, the owner of the farm. "I drove down from the house when I heard you all were here," he said pleasantly. He was a tall, heavy-shouldered man dressed in vintage tweeds plastered with leather patches. His face, seamed with many lines under the patina of a clear, tanned skin, was like old mahogany whose fine scratches lie deep beneath the surface polish. His smile was wide and friendly.

"My wife," Charles told him, "owns a son of your mare, a colt named Wilson Pusey."

"Is that so?" Mr. Tate responded politely, but I saw him flinch just a trifle. "I've often wondered what happened to that one." His tone of voice suggested that he had made his first and only comment on the subject, and that any further discussion would be distasteful to him. "Come on up to the house," he invited, taking me by the arm, "and have a drink before you go. Some people have just dropped in."

The narrow road, bordered by trees on both sides, meandered upward for perhaps a mile through gently rising fields of luxuriant grass divided by old stone fences into a checkerboard of pastures where cattle and horses were grazing. It ended on a high ridge in front of a handsome antebellum mansion overlooking the valley. It was a striking contrast to our unadorned livestock farm in Indiana.

We walked up the low, wide-flung steps and crossed the white-columned veranda. Inside Mr. Tate took us through a superbly proportioned drawing room and led us into a library where pictures of many horses hung. A few people were gathered around the fire; they all seemed to be talking at once. Introductions performed, Mr. Tate handed each of us a silver cup.

"A little wine of the country?" He raised his eyebrows amiably.

The whiskey went down like maple syrup. I sipped mine pleasurably, somewhat surprised that Charles emptied his almost immediately. Alcohol, he had said many times, only inflamed his sinuses.

I sat down beside a diminutive lady who wore her many years as carelessly as the toque, fashioned of velvet pansies, upon her marcelled waves of coral hair. She was perched as a pipit might have perched, on the edge of a sofa cushion. Her name was Mrs. Buffington.

"You horse people?" she asked brightly, including Charles with a quick jerk of her head which almost dislodged the pansies.

"Well, not really," I replied. "One swallow doesn't make a spring, you know, but as a matter of fact . . ."

"I've had dozens of them!" she interrupted before I

could explain about Wilson Pusey. "Got cats now. More fun. Horses always have something the matter with them. Never can run when you want them to." She pointed a small, straight finger at a chubby-cheeked balding man in a double-breasted checked suit standing by the fire, extending his cup for another drink. "That," she announced, "is Mr. Sydney Gassoon-Smith, one of the best authorities on cats in the world. I brought him over from England to give me his opinion of my Abyssinians. Much cheaper than taking 178 cats abroad. Less trouble, too. They are very susceptible to colds." I nodded sympathetically, and emptied my cup.

Next to Mr. Sydney Gassoon-Smith, Mrs. Buffington's other house guest, a ruddy gentleman from Canada whose large mustache was the color of wild strawberries, was speaking with great animation to a dismal-looking fellow who was trying terribly hard to buy a Bimelech mare he had seen on a nearby horse farm. Every little while he would go to the phone and offer the owner a few more thousand dollars, and he could be heard whining into the mouthpiece, "But *why* won't you sell her?" When he returned he looked more dismal than ever.

"All my people are Canadians," the man with the mustache was saying briskly. "We've lived there forever, you might say. My grandmother was a Guelph."

"Really?" the Bimelech man said absently. "I thought they were extinct."

Charles was fingering the collection of coin silver cups Mrs. Tate was showing him, explaining how she had found each one. His face was rather flushed.

"By gad, that's good whiskey!" exclaimed the Canadian, striding over to the bar where Mr. Tate was uncorking another bottle. "Where do you get it?"

Rufus Tate told him that each year he took a few of his own barrels to a friend in a small distillery and had them worked over. "Just for our own use, and for our friends," he said. "It tests around 117 proof. Of course," he added, looking dubiously at his guests, "you don't stay with it all evening."

"None of that firewater for me!" Mrs. Buffington called over from the sofa where we were sitting. "At least not when I'm driving. Last time I left here I sheared off my bumper and a front fender before I got to the main road. Rufus, you must do away with that grove of what-you-macallums at the third turn near the bottom of the hill. They're an unpleasant challenge."

Mr. Tate laughed. "For you, Lavinia, I may just do that, but I'm pretty fond of those trees. Great-granddaddy planted them himself." He looked fondly at the portrait above the mantle where the likeness of a benign old man hung between an engraving of Flora Temple, the trotting mare, and a primitive painting of Bulle Rock, the first thoroughbred imported to this country from England. It was obvious Mr. Tate loved the three equally.

Mr. Gassoon-Smith was holding forth on a breed of cat unfamiliar to me. The name, as he said it, sounded like "Bwermishes."

"A peculiar thing happened in this breed," he said, swaying uncertainly back and forth like a cattail on a broken stalk. "They turned white, absolutely white. Albinism crept in, nobody knows why. Very baffling to the geneticists. But the whole goddam breed turned white." He was very impressed. "They can still be found in certain parts of Asia —the mountain regions, I believe."

I looked across the room at Charles. He was seated now in a wing chair by the fire. His head was resting against the crewel embroidery. His eyes were closed. I could see the torment in his face, the tense, pinched look he gets when his headaches are upon him. All at once his face commenced to blur; his features seemed to be disappearing entirely, and his

176

head moved slowly from one shoulder to the other like a pendulum, one, two, one, two. Putting my drink down quickly on the table, I sat up straight and opened my eyes wide. Charles was gradually taking shape again, but when his head stopped moving it didn't in the least resemble his own. The chin was elongated far below his collar and the knot of his tie; brown ears stood up on either side of his poll; his nostrils quivered in agony. Bare teeth gleamed savagely in his opened mouth.

"Wilson!" I exclaimed, jumping up, "Wilson Pusey!"

I got Charles to his feet with some difficulty. We disengaged ourselves from Mr. Gassoon-Smith who was speaking now on the coat of Abyssinian cats, holding an imaginary hair between his thumb and forefinger. "Each hair shaft," he was saying, "has three distinct colors, running 'orizontally." He clicked his nails. "Like a pousse-café, rather . . ."

Before taking our leave of the Tates we promised to arrange better quarters for Mrs. Buffington's cats the next time a cat show was held in Chicago. "The last time," she said, "it was so cold and drafty they started coughing the night before they were to be judged."

"We'll get you all a guest card at the Racquet Club," Charles said thickly, holding onto his throbbing head.

A few weeks later I went to the racetrack where the colt was in training, taking with me lumps of sugar I had filled with Charles' sinus pills.

The first time I stood at his stall with the proffered sugar cube my hand shook so badly I dropped it. The colt was interested. He watched me bend down, pick it up, and place it again in my hand, palm up. He raised and lowered his head with every move I made. When at last he took the lump he dropped it from his mouth and I had to pick it up again, but soon we both caught on. It was not long before he nickered when he saw me walking down the shedrow.

His trainer said one morning, "That colt's finally beginning to come to himself. Guess it's a good thing we put him up last season. He worked three-quarters in sixteen and change this morning; he's beginning to run like a racehorse. Not such a roughneck as he used to be either." I smiled and doubled the dose.

Then came the afternoon when half a dozen cubes fell out of my purse, and the pills, rolling out of the small holes I'd wedged them in, scattered on the ground. The trainer stood sputtering for a few seconds, red in the face. When the words finally came he wanted to know just what the hell I thought I was doing. "Giving him his medicine," I answered. "He has sinus headaches."

"Headaches? A horse?" he yelled at me. "I never heard of a horse with a headache!"

"That doesn't mean they can't have them if their sinuses are inflamed."

"But I don't think horses *have* sinuses." His anger turned to uneasiness because he had been training for thirty years and didn't know whether horses had sinuses or not. "Of course," he admitted, "if it *was* possible, it might be the reason he quits so bad. Can't get enough oxygen to his lungs. But that's ridiculous. The whole thing's ridiculous!"

The trainer walked a few feet away. He stood there thinking. I picked up the pills and put them back in the sugar.

"Wait!" He lunged at me grabbing both my wrists. "Don't give him any today! I'm going to run him Thursday and a horse can have no medication of any kind for forty-eight hours before he races. It's a rule of every racetrack."

"All right," I agreed. "But we'll steam his head out the morning of the race. That helps sometimes, too. There's no rule against that, is there?"

He didn't answer. Instead, he dropped into his canvas chair under the shedrow and didn't say another word to anybody the rest of the day.

178

The day of the race Wilson Pusey threw his jockey before he left the saddling enclosure. He acted as mean as ever. "Anything that happens today is your fault, not mine," the trainer told me, panting from the exertion of tightening the girths.

The odds board showed the colt at eighty to one.

"Last time," Charles said, stepping up to the corner of the grandstand porch from where the trainer and I were going to watch the race, "he was ninety to one. This is a good sign." He did not call my attention to the handicapper's comment after his name in the newspaper, which read "miserable sort."

The colt broke on top. He opened up a lead of about five lengths.

I dug my elbow in the trainer's ribs.

"Don't mean a thing," he said out of the side of his mouth. "He'll be through at the half, just like always."

But Wilson Pusey wasn't through at the half. He wasn't through until he coasted under the wire, the winner by two and a half lengths.

"I said that colt had come to himself, didn't I?" the trainer cried, stumbling down the stairs in his hurry to get to the winner's circle.

My sides ached from Charles' embrace. "How much did you have on him?" he shouted like a small boy on Christmas morning.

I shook my head. "Not a thing."

But Charles didn't hear me. Holding up his two-dollar mutual ticket he pushed his way through the crowd toward the cashier's window.

I stood in silence giving thanks to Aunt Itty Bit and trying to calculate what the winner's share of the purse would be. Even with my education at the university I was still pretty backward in math.

We drove from the racetrack to the farm, and while I was

getting dinner Charles remarked that it might not be a bad idea to raise a few thoroughbreds in addition to our cattle and hogs. "It might be a real good cash crop," he declared, stirring up a pitcher of martinis. "What do you think?"

" 'Tab for later,' as the handicappers say. We have enough things going now without considering raising horses."

While we were eating dinner the telephone rang, two longs and a short, our ring down on the party line. I got up to answer it. It was a telegram from Maria informing us she had been married that morning.

CHAPTER
16

I wrote down the message delivered by Central with her ever-present throat lozenge clicking against her teeth. It was from Boston where Maria and Florence Harp were in college majoring not in biology, but in sociology.

"You will love Frank," the telegram read. "He is a herpetologist." Maria mentioned the name of a college in Florida I'd never heard of where they were going to live while Frank taught his classes.

When I read the wire to Charles the color left his face. He waved one hand in a gesture of helplessness. "Well," he said quietly, "that's that."

"What's a herpetologist? It sounds like someone who gives scalp treatments."

"It isn't. It's someone who deals in snakes."

"Oh God."

"Let's try to take this in stride," Charles said with little conviction. "At least let's try to get off on the right foot by wiring our congratulations and good wishes to the bride and groom."

"We can't."

"Why not?"

"Because Maria neglected to mention Frank's last name."

Charles sighed and retreated into a deep silence. Finally he said, "I know what we can do. "We'll send Jan to Florida for part of her spring vacation from Miss Sibley's. She'll give us the pitch on Frank when she returns."

Jan squealed her delight over the long distance telephone call Charles put in for her.

"She seemed more pleased about being called out of study hall than about Maria's marriage," Charles remarked when he hung up. "I don't understand the values of the young any more. I must be getting old."

When Jan returned from Florida she gave us a breathless account of her new brother-in-law. "Frank's absolutely *neat*! He has a forehead absolutely bulging with brains, bright red hair, and he's six-feet-six. He keeps a revolting bunch of snakes in pans all over their kitchen, and when he's not messing around with them or teaching classes, he flies birds."

"What do you mean, he flies birds?" Charles demanded.

"He's a falconer. It's his hobby. He keeps a lot of hawks chained to tree stumps in the back yard. He puts on a big leather glove and releases the birds one at a time. The bird flies from his fist, sails through the sky supposedly hunting, and returns to his fist on a whistled command. It's neat, except some of the hawks are crazy about eating snakes so Frank has to be awfully careful of his specimens."

Charles opened his mouth to speak, but closed it without uttering a word.

"How is Maria?" I asked weakly.

"Oh, she's *neat*! She's started a school for Indian children she thinks are underprivileged, and she helps Frank, too. She milks the rattlesnakes for him. He says it saves him a lot of time. They sell the stuff to labs and things."

"What stuff?"

"The venom Maria milks out of the snakes."

I could think of nothing more to say. Neither, apparently, could Charles. We sat there staring at one other like a pair of department store window dummies.

182

After Jan returned to Miss Sibley's, we spent more time than ever at the farm. We simplified our operation to raising corn and soybeans, breeding purebred cattle, and feeding steers and hogs for the commercial market. It was what one of the experts on farm management from the university recommended after looking over the place one Sunday morning. "Stick to this simple plan," he said, "and you may make it."

There were to be no more sidelines such as turkeys. Nor was Charles encouraged to try a corn-potato-mint rotation that had proven very successful at the Red Top Farm. When the mint was harvested and distilled, it was so valuable the barrels were stored in a vault at the bank until they were sold. This impressed Charles, but the human textbook shook his head. "You'll have all you can do just fertilizing this soil and harvesting the crops it will grow. Don't try anything fancy."

One afternoon I returned from Zulu to find Charles escorting two nuns and a priest down the hill from our house to their car in the barnlot. When he motioned me over I went reluctantly. I was especially dirty. Lottie and I had been on our hands and knees on Main Street in town, chalking a diagram and numbers for the cakewalk sponsored by the women in Lottie's lodge. Bully Boy Herburger, the sheriff, had roped off the end of the street for the event, and the housewives in Zulu were busily baking cakes for the prizes. 'Tater Bug Miller had put a new string in his fiddle, and everyone was anticipating a big evening.

I wiped my filthy hand on the seat of my pants before offering it to the nuns.

"Father Joseph and the Mother Superior are interested in buying a farm for a home for the elderly in their church," Charles explained after the introductions. "We've been talking about it in the house."

"How interesting," I said politely, at the same time wondering if they'd seen the two empty bourbon bottles on

183

the sink I hadn't gotten around to throwing out. "I do hope you find one."

Charles raised his eyebrows at me as he helped the nuns into the back seat of the car.

Father Joseph slid under the wheel in front, and turning the ignition key, said to Charles, "It's all set then?"

"I believe you can count on it," Charles replied. "I only want a little more time to think about it—family consideration, you know."

"Of course. We understand. But we want you to know we're ready to go anytime you say the word."

Walking up the hill I asked Charles where he thought he was going to find a farm for the church people to buy.

"I told them I'd sell them this one, if you agreed."

My feet stopped moving. "You must be crazy!" I cried. "You certainly aren't going to sell the farm now, after all the trouble we've been through! We've just started making it pay! What about all the thought we've given it, not to mention the elbow grease and the cold hard cash? It's the silliest thing I've ever heard!"

"Sit down," Charles said when we reached the kitchen. "I want to talk to you."

We faced each other across the oilcloth-covered table.

"In the first place I don't want to sell the farm any more than you do. I enjoy it every bit as much. It has become a way of life that I appreciate in spite of all its troubles. However, I've thought for a long time about the years ahead and the financial insecurity we might find ourselves in if I go on putting into the farm the money I make in the city. Oh, it's all right now. The farm shows a comfortable profit, enough to get along on if we don't have any serious trouble, but a crop failure, an outbreak of Bang's disease in the herd, and any number of other misfortunes could ruin us. Our margin of profit isn't adequate to take care of disasters. We have the satisfaction of having built the place into a paying operation, but that operation isn't sound enough should anything big go wrong.

"We have Jan to think of, too. After she graduates from Miss Sibley's there'll be college. That costs money and I'd like to be able to give her a trip to Europe when the time comes. We weren't able to do it for Maria. Also, I don't know if Frank can support a family on snakes; we might have to give them a hand one day."

"In plain words, you think we ought to sell the farm?"

"I do. This is the first offer we've had for it; there might be others later on, but it could be the only one we'll ever have. If you want to think about it for awhile, why that's all right, but I wouldn't want to miss the market."

Red hot tears smarted my eyes. I tried to speak but my chin trembled and the words were bitten in half by my chattering teeth. I put my head down on the greasy oilcloth and bawled like a spoiled baby.

When at last I straightened up Charles had gone. I saw him out the window climbing on the M to drag the cultivator to the fields. The corn in all but one field was laid by for the year. This was the last one to go. Then with the field work behind us would come the pleasant late summer days, days to visit with neighbors, to go to the fairs, to show our cattle, to enjoy the peacefulness of relative quiet before the autumn harvest began.

Well, what the hell, if it has to be, it has to be, I told myself, wiping my nose on the back of my hand. Maybe I could take up tennis again, or get on a committee of some kind. Maybe Charles and Jan and I could all go to Europe. There were lots of things to do, I told myself. But I couldn't think of a single one that would be as rewarding as our life in Zulu had become.

185

CHAPTER
17

"I can't for the life of me see why you're going to all this fuss." Charles nodded at the mountain of curtains I was washing in the kitchen sink.

"I want to leave the place in order for Father Joseph and his gang. When I get the curtains on the the line I'm going to weed out the closets and drawers."

"Oh, God, you won't be fit to live with tonight. What's the hurry? The papers haven't been signed. We won't have the earnest money for several days, maybe a week."

"Nevertheless, there's a lot to do. We've got to go through that stuff in the Schlagers' attic. I told Father Joseph he could have the blue velour sofa, the one that matches our chair, that we put up there. That has to be brought back. And Uncle Henry's tarpon. What in heaven's name are we going to do with that monstrosity? And you'd better have a look in that old running-board trunk off his Pierce Arrow before we throw it out. That thing has been in Lottie's attic as long as we've been here. I've asked you dozens of times to go through it."

"Just junk." Charles picked up the now abandoned ice pick and started to clean the dirt out of his fingernails.

"I don't care what it is. It's got to be done. Why don't you hitch a wagon box to the tractor and move everything over while I finish the curtains?"

Reluctantly he laid down the ice pick and went out the

kitchen door. A few moments later I heard the M cough to a start, and through the curtainless window I watched him drive slowly up the hill to the Schlagers' back door.

Lottie was chopping wood, but with Charles' arrival she drove the ax into a crotch of oak and left it to pass the time of day with him. The wind caught her scarf, blowing it out behind her neck like a skater's muffler.

How I would miss Lottie! She and Art had decided to stay on as caretakers for the church home, "bein's" as Art declared, "a person can't think of nowhere's else to go that would be near as homelike."

The thought of no longer having the farm was almost unendurable. My heart was as heavy as the soggy muslin curtains I wrung out and threw in the galvanized tub that once held water for Old Mae. Jan used to ride her up to the house after galloping through the woods and across the fields and tether her to the oak tree. After slopping her chin around in the water the mare would push her dripping face against the screen in the opened window, and with ears twitching in curiosity, she'd observe every move I was making in the kitchen.

I couldn't bear to think of leaving the cows; I was fond of every one of them. Many of their calves were now matrons in the herd with calves of their own. In the beginning they were just black beasts identifiable only by numbered chains around their necks. Over the years they had become individuals, personalities each with her own likes, dislikes, temperament, and humor.

In the evenings at dusk we would straddle a gate or corner post in one of the pastures eating a bag of gumdrops from Mamie Tucker's variety store in Zulu and, seeing us, the cows walked slowly over to group up around us, stomping flies and switching their black tasseled tails. They stared at us with their luminous unblinking eyes. The ones in the front

187

row sniffed our boot legs with their moist noses, or wiped their hard flat cheeks across our knees.

I delighted in the fields, the one time filthy acres of black sand now covered with respectable crops; the old red barn, a relic almost, of an era gone by with its cathedral-shaped windows and turquoise ball lightning rods. I would miss the sows grunting at their busy piglets, Enoch shooting his daggers of tobacco juice, Art with his unfailing Hoosier philosophy, and our little house. So much had happened in it! Here we had hatched most of our plans for improving the farm, outlined our experiments on feeding, and drawn the sketches for remodeling sheds and barns to facilitate the handling of stock and storing of grain.

Never again would I wake up looking at the brown smear on the whitewashed ceiling where Charles had swatted a spider as large as my hand. Nor would I grab a clean shirt from the old-fashioned wardrobe listing on its rickety, termite infested legs, or sink at the end of the day into the blue velour chair; most of its stuffing was gone, but it was wonderfully embracing.

The farm had become our life. How could we do without it? What would we do? Could we really adjust to suburban living again? I was being mawkish, but I couldn't help it.

Carrying the tub of wet curtains outdoors to the line I brushed against the Chinese elm tree Charles had bought at Mamie Tucker's for my birthday. It was a homely little thing when he planted it outside the window on my side of the bed; now, with its slender trunk as long as a giraffe's neck stretching to the sky, it was still a homely tree, but along with the spider smear it was there every morning when I opened my eyes, and it was the last silhouette to fade into the deepening evening sky. It was comforting to me.

There was no point in being sentimental, of looking back. We were doing the sensible thing selling the farm to people who would enjoy it.

188

Aunt used to say when we moved about like gypsies, "If you never count on laying your head on the same pillow every night, you will never mind any move you have to make."

Aunt dealt with life with a brisk resourcefulness. She made every new place homelike and pleasant: a few flowers she carried from somewhere wrapped in a damp newspaper; the beds she made up with fresh linen in a twinkling; her stock-in-trade dinners making unfamiliar china somehow familiar. After dinner she would sit down and play "Inskyoff's Parade" or, lacking a piano, open a window and call to the birds which responded to her voice and the feed she put on the sill. Nothing ever fazed Aunt, nor did it seem to faze Mamma who moved from one "home" to another, sometimes charming, more often not, with the grace of an angel and the poise of an aristocrat too proud to acknowledge the shabbiness induced by limited circumstances.

Why, then, should I let this move upset me? All we were doing really was giving up our life at the farm to spend our time in our perfectly good home in Winnetka. It wasn't a change at all. Except it was. We had lost touch with the suburban way of life. When our friends were playing golf or tennis or going to meetings or cocktail parties, we were at the farm, or getting ready to go, or on our way back. We had dropped out of the race for self-promotion, superficial entertainment, social position. Could we ever get back in? Pick up the threads again?

When I asked Charles about this, he laughed. "All you have to do" he said, "is to have a few cocktail parties and you'll be right back where you started."

The thought didn't comfort me.

When the curtains were flapping on the line, I went in to heat up the stew from the night before and to take from the oven a pie made from the apples Uncle Henry's orchard still provided. They were wormy, but they tasted good.

While I was setting the table Charles struggled up the backsteps, his arms closed around the heavy running-board trunk. He set it down with a grunt in the middle of the kitchen floor, and used a bath towel to wipe the dust and cobwebs from it. "I'll just have a look inside," he said. "It won't take a minute."

I helped him lift out handfuls of papers and bundles of letters tied together with grocery string.

"Just as I imagined," he commented, riffling through them. "Nothing but junk. Receipted bills, the blueprints of his house down here, the contractor's specifications, order sheets from restaurants in Chicago for his butter, and letters of complaint from same. Here's an old postcard I sent him from Colorado the summer my scout troop went to Pikes Peak with our leader. I'll never forget how sick I was from the altitude when we got to the top! I threw up for twenty-four hours and I could barely hold my head up long enough to make the trip down. I wonder why Uncle Henry kept that postcard?"

He started to return the papers to the trunk when we saw between the folds of an old newspaper lining the bottom a long brown envelope. It had Charles' name on it in Uncle Henry's flowing handwriting.

"Hmm," said Charles, and reaching for a kitchen knife he slit it open. He took out a three-page letter on stationery from Uncle Henry's old business firm. It was dated two days prior to his last trip to Paris to visit Cousin Will Webb. I read the letter over Charles' shoulder.

Dear Charles,

By the time you open this envelope that pompous ass, Milton Phillips, will have read my will which, as my attorney, he has brought up to date and put in proper order. There's nothing Phillips likes better than to read the will of one of his old cronies he has outlived. It makes him feel superior.

At any rate you now know that the farm in Indiana described in my will in eight pages—these lawyers can't say anything in a few words—is yours.

In case you wonder why I want you to have it, I shall explain.

First, Millicent would gain nothing from it, nor it from her. It would be an unsuitable legacy.

Second, Robert lives in New York. What good would a farm in Indiana do him? He'd sell it, or give it away. He has become, as I myself became to my regret, so involved in business he is now incapable of thinking about anything else.

Third, Henry, Jr., is incompetent. He will have money to provide him with the medical care he needs which I suppose he will spend on drink. He has, unfortunately, taken after your poor Aunt Charlotte's father whom you never knew. He was a worse offender than Henry, Jr. When he was under the influence of alcohol he became involved in some unsavory escapades, one of which led to a jail sentence. Your poor Aunt Charlotte never recovered from that blow.

That leaves you and your wife, Mary. I believe you chose wisely. Mary is a sensible girl for the most part and I believe she will stay with you through the thick and thin of life.

You, Charles, have always had a feeling for the soil and what it produces. You demonstrated this with commendable practicality when you were ten years old and sold the sweet peas you raised on the wire fence at Rollingwood to commuters on the station platform for five cents a bunch! How I chuckled at that!

Having the farm is going to pull you off your city job now and again, but that will be good for you. (I wish I had had this farm when I was a young man; it would have enriched my life.) I am entirely aware of the problems you will have to contend with trying to do both, especially at first when you are learning what the farm will best produce. I have failed with the crops I tried to grow, the dairy, the orchards, everything, in fact, that I attempted, but I am an old man, and like Robert, too rigid, too

191

limited in my thinking, to succeed in the usual sense of the word in an undertaking unfamiliar to me.

However, I have learned one thing while I have been living alone down here, and that is that the land is good for a man's soul. I guess it always has been. The way things are going in the world today and the behavior of the human race in general, a man had better start paying some attention to his soul if he expects to look his Maker in the eye.

If you stick with this place, Charles, and farm the land as it should be farmed, it will give you a way of life which is as worthwhile, as nourishing as a good pot of beans. I believe it eventually will bring you the kind of gratification that comes from simple honest things, not the cheap things men sometimes do in your business and in mine.

I realize it will take money to set up whatever program you decide upon, and that is why you will find in this envelope which I will put in my safe-deposit vault at the bank where my will and other papers are, three United States Government bonds with all coupons attached, in the value of $100,000 each. One is to use on the farm. One is for yourself, and the third is for your wife, Mary. All women need a few frills and furbelows to keep them happy, even the good ones.

You may wonder how I came to get the farm in the first place. Do you recall the South Lake Bank, that small bank of which I was one of the directors? With the crash of '29 came the run on all banks, and this little fellow couldn't meet the demands of its depositors. That meant that men who had worked for me at the plant, and who had put their money in this bank because I was a director, weren't going to get it back. I couldn't let that happen. I put up my own money to cover them. In turn I received the only assets the bank had, one of which was a mortgage on the farm in Indiana. It is the best legacy I've ever had, and I only wish it had come to me sooner.

I hope it will prove rewarding to you and Mary who are

192

*young enough to put your shoulders to the wheel which you
must do in order to receive its full benefits.*

*I am not a demonstrative man, Charles, but I want you to
know that you have been closer to me than my own sons. You
have given me hope, affection, and your trust. I return them to
you now.*

The letter was signed simply, *"Uncle H."*

"I'll be goddamned." Charles let the pages slip from his
hands to the floor. Getting up he walked to the window and
stared out at the east pasture. "You know," he began, and
turning around interrupted himself, changing the tone of his
voice. "Why, Mary, you're crying!" He put his arms around
me over the busted back of the kitchen chair. "I don't see
what there is to cry about. We can stay here the rest of our
lives now if we want to. We can enlarge the purebred herd,
increase our steer operation, and buy all the machinery we
need. We can even build a new house if you'd like to. For
God's sake, stop crying!"

"I can't help it. I keep thinking about Uncle Henry."

"What about Uncle Henry?"

"I always misunderstood him. I doubted him. I hated him
in the beginning for saddling us with this place. I thought he
was unreasonable."

"Uncle Henry always had a reason for everything he did.
I was so dumb it took me a long time to find out about this
one. That wasn't his fault."

Charles picked up the bonds, examining them carefully
before tossing them on the knee of my blue jeans. "Obviously the fact that these bonds were in bearer form and none
of the coupons had ever been cashed was the reason why this
part of Uncle Henry's estate was never uncovered by any
one. What a break for us!"

"Think where we'd be if Art hadn't saved this old trunk
and the tarpon when the house burned down."

193

"That," said Charles, "is something I won't permit myself to think about! Right now I feel we ought to celebrate. It's a pity there's no champagne in Muskrat County."

"Zulu has its own kind of wine. Better than champagne."

I opened the door of the cabinet above the stove. Together we stood laughing at the shiny brown crock of freshly-baked beans Lottie had brought over that morning. She had told me, "I reckon movin' is a mite wearyin'. I figured youse might piece off these here beans."

I'd learned that in Muskrat County the plural of "you" is "youse." I'd learned a lot of other things as well.

194

About the author . . .

Mary Scott Adams is the pen name of Priscilla D. Willis. The material in SIX TO BREAK EVEN is based on the experiences she and her family had farming in Indiana while at the same time trying to maintain a normal suburban life in Winnetka.

Farming, Mrs. Willis says, has probably been the greatest single adventure of her life, worrisome, yet wonderfully rewarding. After the war, the farming operation was moved from Indiana to south Georgia where the Willis family bred and raised cattle until three years ago.

They now live in an apartment in downtown Chicago, but their interest in livestock continues in a small stable of horses which they race in Chicago and Florida. Mrs. Willis has written articles and short stories for *Harper's*, *Reader's Digest*, and other magazines and is the author of several children's books.

PRINTED IN U.S.A.